P9-DMW-185

Miss Mary Louise Mann

Erwin Owen
8 (c)

THE
HALCYON
SONG-BOOK

COMPILED AND ARRANGED

BY

LEONARD B. MARSHALL

ASSISTANT DIRECTOR OF MUSIC IN THE
BOSTON PUBLIC SCHOOLS

SILVER, BURDETT & COMPANY

NEW YORK   BOSTON   CHICAGO

Copyright, 1909,

By SILVER, BURDETT & COMPANY

In addition to the original songs,
poems and arrangements copyrighted
separately, this volume contains much
other original material which is cov-
ered by the general copyright of the
book and must not be used without
special permission.

PREFACE

THE HALCYON SONG-BOOK has a twofold purpose: to inspire the pupil to sing well, and to cultivate his musical appreciation. It aims, through arousing in the pupil a desire to sing, to give the teacher and the supervisor the best possible foundation for their work. In gathering the work of the older masters and of the foremost modern composers, great care has been taken that the songs be not only interesting in melody and rich in harmony, but that they shall make a sympathetic appeal to the varied sensibilities of the pupil. Much of the music and much of the poetry has been written expressly for this book. In some cases new musical settings have been made for selections from famous poets. Numerous songs for special occasions and for the days which are celebrated throughout this country, have been composed particularly for this collection. In response to suggestions from many teachers a few rousing athletic songs have been provided.

The book is especially designed for use in high schools and upper grammar grades; and the unusual variety in the arrangement of the songs makes it useful in schools where there are both boys and girls and where some of the boys' voices have not changed. There are unison songs, songs with an optional bass, two-part and three-part songs and a wide variety of four-part choruses. The songs with the melody in the bass are designed to quicken the enthusiasm of the boys, and to make them feel that they are a component and important part in the organization of the school chorus. The songs for this purpose have been selected to suit the boy's powers and appeal to his imagination.

As a concluding portion of the book a group of the popular songs of this and other countries has been included, in the hope that they will serve to create an atmosphere of joyousness in the school-room.

The Halcyon contains new songs by the following well-known Americans: George W. Chadwick, Henry Hadley, Harvey Worthington Loomis, W. W. Gilchrist, Charles Fonteyn Manney, H. Clough-Leighter, Carrie Bullard, George B. Nevin, George A. Burdett, George Henry Howard, and George Lowell Tracy.

Great credit, with hearty acknowledgments, is due the following authors for the untiring pains bestowed upon the large number of poems

3

written for this book: Nixon Waterman, David Kilburn Stevens, Clinton Scollard, Margaret E. Sangster, J. Annie Bense, Henry Rivers, George F. Morton, Herbert B. Englemann and others.

It is a pleasure to recognize the helpful suggestions received from a large number of educators, including many eminent Directors and Supervisors of Music, whose advice has assisted the editor in meeting the varying needs of pupils under the conditions found in the different school systems of the country.   Special mention should be made of the suggestions from Samuel W. Cole, New England Conservatory of Music, Boston; Alfred Hallam, Mount Vernon; S. Henry Hadley, Somerville; Grant Drake, Boston; Dr. Albert G. Mitchell, Boston; Alice J. Garthe, Chicago; Herbert Griggs, New York; J. F. McCullough, Chicago; T. L. Roberts, Utica; M. E. Chase, Malden; Bessie M. Salmon, Boston.

The valuable assistance of Leo R. Lewis, George Henry Howard and George Lowell Tracy in the arrangement of the music contained in this volume, should also be gratefully acknowledged.

Thanks are due Houghton, Mifflin & Company, The Century Company and Little, Brown & Company, for permission to use copyrighted poems.

That this volume may contribute in a large way to the pleasure and profit of the young people throughout the country is the earnest wish of the editor.

LEONARD B. MARSHALL

Boston, *September, 1909*

THE HALCYON SONG-BOOK

The Year's at the Spring

ROBERT BROWNING

CHARLES FONTEYN MANNEY

Moderately fast and with spirit

mf The year's at the spring, And day's at the morn; Morn - ing's at sev - en;

The

The lark's on the wing, ..

mf *cres.*

The hill - side's dew - pearl'd;

The

hill - side's dew - pearl'd; ..

on the wing;

snail's on the thorn: God's in his heav - en, All's right with the world.

world, God's in his

world. . . . . .

cres. ed allarg.

God's in his heav - en, All's right, all's right with the world, with the world.

heav'n,

world. . . . . .

Copyright, 1909, by SILVER, BURDETT & COMPANY

(5)

To the Rose
Unison Song for Medium Voices

Nixon Waterman

Adolf Jensen

1. O, rose of June, thou art so fair! Thy
2. Fair queen of flow'rs art thou, O, rose! Thy

beau - ty our be - ing en - tran - ces, As through the sweet, . . bloom=scent-ed
sis - ters, how - e'er we may love them, When thou thy match - less charms dis -

air, The but - ter - fly mer - ri - ly dan - ces. And when from the
close, Must hold thee in beau - ty a - bove them. And when on thy

Copyright, 1909, by Silver, Burdett & Company

The Ingle=side

Three-Part Song, with Melody in the Bass

HEW AINSLIE

T. V. WIESENTHAL
Arr. by C. B. RICH

* Ingle-side means fire-side; burnie, brook; gowans, daisies; haughs, meadows; canty, gay.

Copyright, 1909, by SILVER, BURDETT & COMPANY

green hill - side,   Where hums the bon - - nie bee, ...
cro - nies meet,   The dar - ling o' . . . our e'e, ...

green   hill - side,   Where hums the bon - nie bee, . . But rar - er
cro - nies meet,   The dar - ling o' . . . our e'e, . . That makes to

green hill - side   Where hums   the bon - ny   bee,   But
cro - nies meet,   An' the dar - ling o'   our   e'e,   That

.. But rar - er,   but fair - er,   but fin - er far   Is the in - gle = side for   me.

far, but rar - er,   but fair - er,   but fin - er far   Is the in - gle = side   for   me.

rar - er, fair - er,   fin - er   far   Is the in - gle = side   for   me.

. That makes   to   us   a warl' com - plete; O . . the in - gle = side's for me.

us, that makes   to   us   a warl' com - plete; O the in - gle = side's for   me.

makes   to us   a warl' com - plete; O the in - gle = side's for   me.

The Windmill

Solo for Medium Voice, with Chorus

David Kilburn Stevens

H. Clough–Leighter

1. The wind-mill stands by the fer - tile plain, Where the breez-es fresh-ly blow; And he sees the prom-ised fields of grain As the care-ful farm-ers sow. And when the wind from o'er the craft The
2. The gold-en days of the sum-mer fade, And the reap-ers now ap-pear; While the ripe grain falls to shin-ing blade, And crowns the fruit-ful year. The wind-mill shakes his i - dle sails, And
3. The treas-ures rich in his cof-fers roll, But no mis-er grim is he, He re-stores it, save the mod-est dole Which he keeps for his law-ful fee. Now, tho' the cold earth lie a-sleep, He

Copyright, 1909, by Silver, Burdett & Company

rah! . . . . 30 . . . .

rah for the glow of the yel - low corn! Hur - rah for the field of rye! . . It will
3D VERSE. Hur - rah for the gold - en grain! .

poco meno mosso 34 rall. 1st and 2d ending a tempo

all be mine, I will grind it fine, For har - vest = time is nigh! . .
3D VERSE. When the

1st and 2d ending

poco meno mosso 34 rall. f a tempo

ff 40

Ped. ✳ Ped. ✳ Ped. ✳ Ped. ✳

44 D.C. 3d ending

har - vest comes a - gain! . .

3d ending

44 a tempo D.C.

mf poco rit. f

Ped. ✳

My Native Land

Song for Medium Voice, with Four-Part Chorus

Alfred C. Page

From "A Trip to Africa" by Von Suppé

1. A rest-less wan-der-er, . . whose wea-ry feet . . So long have pressed the soil of dis-tant strand, . With night how oft there comes, . . my dreams to greet, . A vis-ion of my own dear Na - tive Land!
2. In smil-ing fields I breathe the fra-grant air, . . Thro' val-ley green I roam, or for-est grand; . But O! there is no ver-tdure a-ny-where . Like vale and for-est in my Na - tive Land.
3. Tho' won-ders rare are seen . a-cross the sea, . . Tho' a-lien shores may wave a beck-'ning hand, . There is no path I tread so fair to me . . As that which leads me to my Na - tive Land.

Copyright, 1909, by Silver, Burdett & Company

* Upper notes for changed voices; lower notes for unchanged voices.

Greetings

Two-Part Song for Equal* Voices

C. Eyserbeck
Andantino

Franz Abt

FIRST VOICE

1. Who is the boy with gold-en hair? At dawn he comes with looks so fair, It
2. To my be-lov-ed home do fly, To my dear friends, O sun-beam,hie, Say
3. And if they sad and lone-ly seem, Then, sun-shine,send your bright-est beam, Tell

SECOND VOICE

is the Spring sun's first bright ray, It is the Spring sun's first bright ray.
that I fond-ly think of them, Say that I fond-ly think of them.
them we soon shall meet a-gain, Tell them we soon shall meet a-gain.

SECOND VOICE

It is the Spring sun's first bright ray. O
Say that I fond-ly think of them. O
Tell them we soon shall meet a-gain. O

* Equal voices are those of the same general register. Thus, this number is suitable for Soprano and Contralto, or for Tenor and Bass; but not for Soprano and Bass, or Tenor and Contralto.

O sun-beam, wel-come be, A thousand greetings take from me. O

dear - est sun - beam, wel - come be, A thou-sand greet - ings take from me. O

dear - est sun - beam, wel - come be, ... A thou - sand greet - ings take from

dear - est sun - beam, wel - come be, . . A thou-sand, thou - sand greet - ings take from

me, A thou-sand greetings, A thou-sand greetings take from me.

me, A thousand greet-ings, A thou-sand greetings take from me.

To the Nightingale

Unison Song

NIXON WATERMAN   HALFDAN KJERULF

1. Sing, sing, night-in-gale, sing, Soft - ly the shad-ows are fall - ing;
2. Trill, trill, night-in-gale, trill, While your sweet dream you are tell - ing —
3. Dream, dream, night-in-gale, dream, Safe in your green leaf-y bow - er;

Gent - ly your mel - o - dy goes,   Stir - ring the heart of the rose; Sing, oh,
Stars in their heav - en a - bove,   Look on the val - leys they love; Trill, oh,
Bath - ing the vales with her light, Comes the fair queen of the night; Dream, oh,

sing, your fond mate is call - - ing.
trill, your mu - sic up - well - - ing.
dream, with bud and with flow - - er.

The Age of Gold

M. J. SAVAGE
ROBERT VOLKMANN

1. The God that to the fa - thers Re-veal'd His ho - ly will Has not the world for-
2. 'Twas but far off, in vis - ion, The fa - thers' eyes could see The glo - ry of the
3. With trust in God's free spir - it,—The ev - er=broad-'ning ray Of truth that shines to

sak - en, He's with the chil - dren still. Then en - vy not the twi - light That
king - dom,—The bet - ter time to be. To - day we see ful - fill - ing The
guide us A - long our for-ward way,—Let us to - day be faith - ful As

glim-mer'd on their way; Look up, and see the dawn - ing That broad-ens in - to day!
dreams they dreamt of old; While near - er, ev - er near - er, Rolls on the age of gold.
were the brave of old, Till we, their work com-plet - ing, Bring in the age of gold!

At Close of Day

Unison Song

GEORGE Y. HUME

HARVEY WORTHINGTON LOOMIS

1. While the twi-light sha-dows Gath-er o'er the mead-ows; When the crim-son
2. As the day is dy-ing, Swal-lows home-ward fly-ing; One by one the

sun has gone to rest; Vil-lage chimes are ring-ing; Whip-poor-wills are
stars ap-pear a-bove. On the dream-ing riv-er Sil-ver moon-beams

sing-ing; Pur-ple clouds are sink-ing low in the west.
quiv-er; Heav'n is shed-ding o'er the earth peace and love.

Copyright, 1909, by SILVER, BURDETT & COMPANY

The Bright Rosy Morning

Three-Part Song, with Melody in the Bass

The Earl of Oxford

Old English Air
Arr. by C. B. Rich

Copyright, 1909, by Silver, Burdett & Company

Ship of State

Henry W. Longfellow   George Lowell Tracy

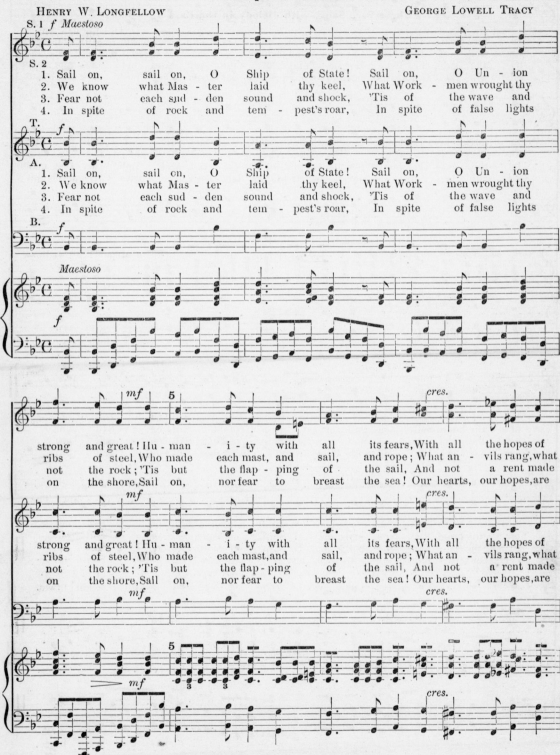

1. Sail on, sail on, O Ship of State! Sail on, O Un - ion
2. We know what Mas - ter laid thy keel, What Work - men wrought thy
3. Fear not each sud - den sound and shock, 'Tis of the wave and
4. In spite of rock and tem - pest's roar, In spite of false lights

strong and great! Hu - man - i - ty with all its fears, With all the hopes of
ribs of steel, Who made each mast, and sail, and rope; What an - vils rang, what
not the rock; 'Tis but the flap - ping of the sail, And not a rent made
on the shore, Sail on, nor fear to breast the sea! Our hearts, our hopes, are

Copyright, 1909, by Silver Burdett & Company

10
fu - ture years, Is hang - ing breath-less on thy fate. Sail on, sail on, O
ham - mers beat, In what a forge and what a heat Were shap'd the an - chors
by the gale. 'Tis but the flap - ping of the sail, And not a rent made
all with thee. Our hearts, our hopes, our pray'rs, our tears, Our faith tri - umph -ant
fu - ture years, Is hang - ing breath-less on thy fate. Sail on, sail on, O
ham - mers beat, In what a forge and what a heat Were shap'd the an - chors
by the gale. 'Tis but the flap - ping of the sail, And not a rent made
all with thee. Our hearts, our hopes, our pray'rs, our tears, Our faith tri - umph -ant
10
f
15
Ship of State, Sail on, O Un - ion strong and great, Sail on, Sail on.
of thy hope. Sail on, Sail on, O Ship of State, Sail on, Sail on.
by the gale. Sail on, Sail on, O Ship of State, Sail on, Sail on.
o'er our fears, Are all with thee, are all with thee! Sail on, Sail on.
f
Ship of State, Sail on, O Un - ion strong and great, Sail on, Sail on.
of thy hope. Sail on, Sail on, O Ship of State, Sail on, Sail on.
by the gale. Sail on, Sail on, O Ship of State, Sail on, Sail on.
o'er our fears, Are all with thee, are all with thee! Sail on, Sail on.
f
15
f

The Spinning Wheel

Song for Medium Voice, with Chorus for Equal Voices

David K. Stevens

Charles Fonteyn Manney

Not too fast, smoothly

1. By an o - pen cot - tage win-dow, where the summer rose is fair, And hon - ey = la - den
2. The bee is in the clo - ver and a - mong the trump-et vines, The humming-bird is
3. And when the clos - ing sha-dows mark the end - ing of the day, The spin - ner stops her

li - lacs scent the ear - ly morn - ing air, Where va - grant lit - tle sun-beams thro' the
bus - y where the hon - ey - suck - le twines; And min-gling with the mel - o - dy that
wheel and puts the card - ed wool a - way; But when the dawn is break-ing, and an -

leaf - y trel - lis steal, The bus - y spin - ner, all the day, is sing-ing at her
lark and thrush pro-long, From out the o - pen win - dow comes the cease - less spin - ning
oth - er day is come, The wheel a - gain is whirl - ing with its ev - er bus - y

Copyright, 1909, Silver, Burdett & Company

wheel: Spin, spin, spin! With bus-y, fly-ing fin-gers;
song:
hum:

Days are long in sun-ny June, spin, spin, spin, spin,

spin, spin, spin, While bright day lin - gers;

The Spinning Wheel

Win - ter nights are com - ing soon, spin, spin, spin!

To a Star

Unison Song for Medium or Low Voices

Nixon Waterman

L. B. Marshall

Andante espressivo

1. When night's dark cur -tain veils the sky, Oh, star! thou gleamest from on high; From
2. As thou to us, when viewed a - far, So earth, to thee, is but a star; Oh,
3. A kin - dred, thou, of us and ours; The sky with worlds, the fields with flow'rs, Were

dark till dawn thy light doth shine In beau - ty con - stant and di - vine.
hast thou might - y tribes that see And think on us, as we on thee?
strewn by One whose works they are, With thee and us, oh, won - drous star!

Copyright, 1909, by Silver, Burdett and Company

The Winds of March

WILLIAM HENRY BANCROFT

GEORGE B. NEVIN

1. Blow loud your storm-y trump-ets, Ye li-on=heart-ed gales, Through all the fields and wood-lands, And through the mountain vales. I love to hear your mu-sic A-cross the mead-ows roar, For ye are but the her-alds That come the Spring be-fore.

2. Ye tell of burst-ing or-chards, Of A-pril's jew-eled show'rs, And of the fields be-deck-ing Them-selves with grass and flow'rs; Of brooks and stream-lets flow-ing A-long their course in glee, And riv-ers, once im-pris-oned, On=leap-ing to the sea.

3. Then blow your storm-y trump-ets, Ye prin-ces in dis-guise, And come like those in fa-bles, To o-pen dreaming eyes, To wake the sleep-ing beau-ties In Win-ter's cas-tle strong, Un-til their spell is bro-ken, And thro' its gates they throng.

Copyright, 1909, by SILVER, BURDETT & COMPANY

The Edelweiss

Three-Part Song for Equal Voices

J. Annie Bense

Friedrich Kücken

1. When the moun-tain peaks burn with rose, When the gold-en east flam-ing glows, All the depths be-low lie a-sleep, While the dark, gloomy mists vig-ils keep; Then the wild winds blow From the heights of snow, As they rise . . To the skies. Then the yo-del clear Of the moun-tain-eer, Yo-ho, ho, yo-ho, ho, Wakes ech-o free, Yo-ho, . . Yo-ho, Yo-ho!

2. "On the crest-ed height's sun-lit sea Blooms a no-ble flow'r all for thee!" In the vale be-low dawns the day, And the pure, pearl-y mists steal a-way. Still the glad voice sings, And the ech-o rings; Sweet the cry . . From on high. For one wakes to hear Still the yo-del clear, Yo-ho, ho, yo-ho, ho, "Pure flow'rs for thee," Yo-ho, . . Yo-ho, Yo-ho!

(Soprano 2 reads text with Alto)

La, la, la, la, la, la, la, la, la, la, lee, Yo-ho, . . Yo-ho, . . Yo-ho!

A Moonlight Phantasy

Three-Part Song, for Soprano, Alto, and Bass

J. Annie Bense

W. A. Mozart

Copyright, 1909, by Silver, Burdett & Company

The Pilot

Bass Solo or Unison Song, with Four-Part Chorus

Thornton W. Standish

Stephen Russell

1. In win-ter's night or a sum-mer's day, Blow high or low on the sea's high-way, The Pi-lot rides the wave; . . . His ti-ny craft is staunch and true, And fear-less-ly his hard-y crew Their dai-ly per-ils brave. . . . . . .

2. The wea-ry ves-sel that, tem-pest=toss'd, A thou-sand wa-ter-y leagues has cross'd, Its port is draw-ing near; . . . And soon they hear a heart-y hail, From a craft with a number on her sail, And an-swer with a cheer. . . . . . .

3. He climbs the lad-der and takes command; The Captain and crew at his or-ders stand, The Pi-lot rules su-preme; . . . Now straight and true the ship he guides, Till in-to port she safe-ly glides And anchors in the stream. . . . . . .

Copyright, 1909, by Silver, Burdett & Company

"Hard a - lee" and she comes a - bout, Stand by! The Pi - lot is com-ing a-board! A - hoy!!

"Hard a - lee" and she comes a - bout, Stand by! The Pi - lot is com-ing a-board! A - hoy!!

"Hard a - lee" and she comes a - bout, Stand by! The Pi - lot is com-ing a-board! A - hoy!!

a - hoy!   a - hoy!

The Volunteers

Four-Part Song, with Solo for Tenor-Alto

CHARLES HARVEY   HARVEY WORTHINGTON LOOMIS

Vivace e marziale

Tramp, tramp, tramp, tramp, tramp, tramp, tramp, tramp, tramp, tramp, tramp, tramp, tramp, tramp,

1. A - down the street, With ea - ger
2. To beat of drum, The sol - diers

Tramp, tramp, tramp, tramp, tramp, tramp, tramp, tramp, tramp, tramp, tramp, tramp, tramp, tramp,

Copyright, 1909, by SILVER, BURDETT & COMPANY

tramp, tramp. A - mid our cheers, March the Vol-un - teers ! They nev - er shirk The
Their hearts are true As the sky is blue ; The flag they bear Is

feet, A - mid our cheers, March the Vol-un-teers ! Mu-sic of drums . . Thundering
come, Their hearts are true As the sky is blue ; Trumpet and fife . . . Add to the

tramp, tramp. A - mid our cheers, March the Vol-un - teers ! Crowds are cry - ing And
Their hearts are true As the sky is blue ; Hearts are thrill - ing And

They're
The

brunt of work, And naught ap - pals, When the Na - tion calls.
flaunt - ing fair, The em - blem bright, With the stars be - dight.

comes. . . . O there is naught ap - pals, When the Na - tion calls.
life. . . . . That is the em - blem bright, With the stars be - dight.

caps are fly - ing. O naught ap - pals, When the Na - tion calls.
eyes are fill - ing. The em - blem bright, With the stars be - dight.

The Farmer Boy

Three-Part Song for Equal Voices

ROBERT W. MERRICK

WILHELM TAUBERT

1. The farm-er boy at break of day Sings gay-ly on his ear-ly way A live-ly round-e-lay, ... While from the tree near by Mer-ry lark and thrush re-ply, And as ear-ly birds all do, Sing "Good morn-ing! Good morn-ing! An ex-cel-lent Good morn-ing to you!"

2. Be-side his path in fresh ar-ray, The ear-ly flow-ers, fair and gay, A-wake to hear his lay. . . . . They rise from moss-y beds And shake their dew-y heads And, as ear-ly flow-ers do, Nod "Good morn-ing! Good morn-ing! An ex-cel-lent Good morn-ing to you!"

3. His heart, with joy of liv-ing glad, "Good morn-ing!" shouts the farm-er lad, And ends his round-e-lay; . . . . While from the rock-y hill Comes the voice of Ech-o shrill, And, as ear-ly ech-oes do, Calls "Good morn-ing! Good morn-ing! An ex-cel-lent Good morn-ing to you!"

The Snowdrop

Three-Part Song for Equal Voices

EDWARD OXENFORD

CIRO PINSUTI

A Warrior Bold

Three-Part Song, with Melody in the Bass

Edwin Thomas

Stephen Adams
Arr. by C. B. Rich

Copyright, 1909, by Silver, Burdett & Company

young and fair,   My love hath gold - en hair,   And eyes so
ring he wore   Was crush'd and wet . . with gore;   Yet, ere he

fair,   My love hath eyes so blue, and heart so
ring   Was crush'd; yet, ere he died, he brave-ly

fair,   My love hath gold - en hair,   And eyes so blue, and
wore   Was crush'd and wet with gore;   Yet, ere he died, he

blue, and heart so true,   That none with her com-pare!   So what care
died, he brave-ly cried: "I've kept the vow I swore.   So what care

true, ...   That none with her com-pare! So what care I,   tho'
cried: . . . .   "I've kept the vow I swore. So what care I,   tho'

heart so true   That none with her com - pare!   So what care I,   tho'
brave - ly cried: "I've kept the vow I swore.   So what care I,   tho'

I, tho' death be nigh, I'll live for love, for love I'll die;   So what care
I, tho' death be nigh, I've fought for love, for love I die;   So what care

death be nigh, I'll live for love, for love . . I'll die; So what care I tho'
death be nigh, I've fought for love, for love . . I die; So what care I tho'

death be nigh, I'll live for love or die;   So what care I tho'
death be nigh, I've fought for love and die;   So what care I tho'

My Old Kentucky Home

Four-Part Song, with Melody in the Bass

S. C. FOSTER

S. C. FOSTER
Arr. by C. B. RICH

1. The sun shines bright in the old Kentuck-y Home,   'Tis sum-mer, the dark-ies are
2. They hunt no more for the pos-sum and the coon   On the meadow, the hill and the
3. The head must bow, and the back will have to bend,   Wher-ev-er the dark-y may

Copyright, 1909, by SILVER, BURDETT & COMPANY

My Old Kentucky Home

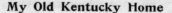

Napoli
Two-Part Song for Equal Voices

NIXON WATERMAN

LUIGI CARACCIOLO

1. Fair Na-ples,'neath your skies of soft-est az-ure,You dream a-
2. By day or night,'neath sun or star re-pos-ing,Your vine-clad
3. When o'er your fes-tal scenes with glad-ness glow-ing,The mel-low

bove your bay whose charm en-tranc-ing, A-wak-ens in the breast a thrill of
hills lead up to shin-ing moun-tains.Your ma-ny wind-ing streets with grace dis-
moon with ra-diant glance is beam-ing. 'Tis then, with life and beau-ty o-ver-

pleasure,When o'er the waves the hap-py sails are danc-ing. Such light and lus-ter,
clos-ing Your thousand gar-dens glad with fruits and foun-tains. Such light and lus-ter,
flow-ing,You seem a vis-ion fashioned 'mid our dream-ing. Such light and lus-ter,

Copyright, 1909, by SILVER, BURDETT & COMPANY

A - round you clus - ter, Ah . . . .

. . . . Your charms are rar - est, rar - est,

of ci - ties you are fair - - est.

Home, Sweet Home

John Howard Payne

Henry R. Bishop

1. 'Mid pleas-ures and pal-a-ces, though we may roam; Be it ev-er so hum-ble, there's no place like home; A charm from the sky seems to hal-low us there, Which, seek thro' the world, is ne'er met with else-where.

2. An ex-ile from home, splen-dor daz-zles in vain; O . . give me my low-ly thatched cot-tage a-gain! The birds sing-ing gay-ly, that come at my call, Give me them and that peace of mind, dear-er than all!

3. To thee I'll re-turn o-ver-bur-dened with care, The . . heart's dear-est sol-ace will smile on me there; No more from that cot-tage a-gain will I roam, Be it ev-er so hum-ble, there's no place like home.

Home, Sweet Home

Home,   home, sweet, sweet home, There's no place like home,   there's no   place like home.

Home,   home, sweet, sweet home, There's no place like home,   there's no   place like home.

Eventide

Three-Part or Four-Part Song (Optional Bass)

STANLEY C. WORCESTER   EDUARD LASSEN

Very slowly and with deep feeling

S. 2

1. Be - yond the hill now sinks the west - ern sun, . The dark - 'ning shad-ows si - lent
2. cross the lake   a   sil - v'ry thread   is   spun, All trem - bling from the   ev - 'ning
3. soon, ap - par - el'd like the shroud - ed nun, Fair Na - ture hides her face from

A.

1. Be - yond   the   hill now sinks the west - ern sun, The dark - 'ning shadows si - lent
2. cross the lake   a   sil - v'ry thread   is   spun, All trem - bling from the   ev - 'ning
3. soon, ap - par - el'd like the shroud - ed nun, Fair Na - ture hides her face from

Op. B.

fall, . While peace de-scends on   all. . . . .   The day is done.   2. A-
star . That pale - ly gleams a - far; . . . .   The day is done.   3. And
view, And   sheds her tears of   dew ; . . .   The day is (*Omit . . .*) done.

fall. . While peace de-scends on   all. . . . .   The day is done.   2. A-
star . That pale - ly gleams a - far; . . . .   The day is done.   3. And
view, And   sheds her tears of   dew ;. . . .   The day is (*Omit . .*) done.

The Happy Miller

Unison Song for Basses, with Four-Part Chorus

David K. Stevens

Allegro vivace

Arthur Sullivan

Bass Solo, or Unison Chorus

1. In a shel-tered vale Lives a mil-ler hale, And the mill-race churn-ing, Keeps the bus-y wheel a-turn-ing, And the val-ley rings, As the mil-ler sings: "While the bus-y wheel is turn-ing And a pen-ny I am earn-ing, Trou-ble

2. To the shel-tered vale Comes the win-ter gale, And the hearth-fire's burn-ing, But the wheel's no lon-ger turn-ing; "Nev-er mind the gale!" Sings the mil-ler hale; "While the fire is bright-ly burn-ing Tho' there's ne'er a mill-wheel turn-ing, Hun-ger

Copyright, 1909, by Silver, Burdett and Company

lit - tle I have lent, O, my wheel has turned for ma - ny, And has

turned an hon - est pen - ny, So my dai - ly song As the riv - er runs a - long Is

"What care I? What care I?" I?" . . . . . .

March, March Along

Unison Song for Medium or Low Voices

GEORGE F. MORTON | GEORGE W. CHADWICK

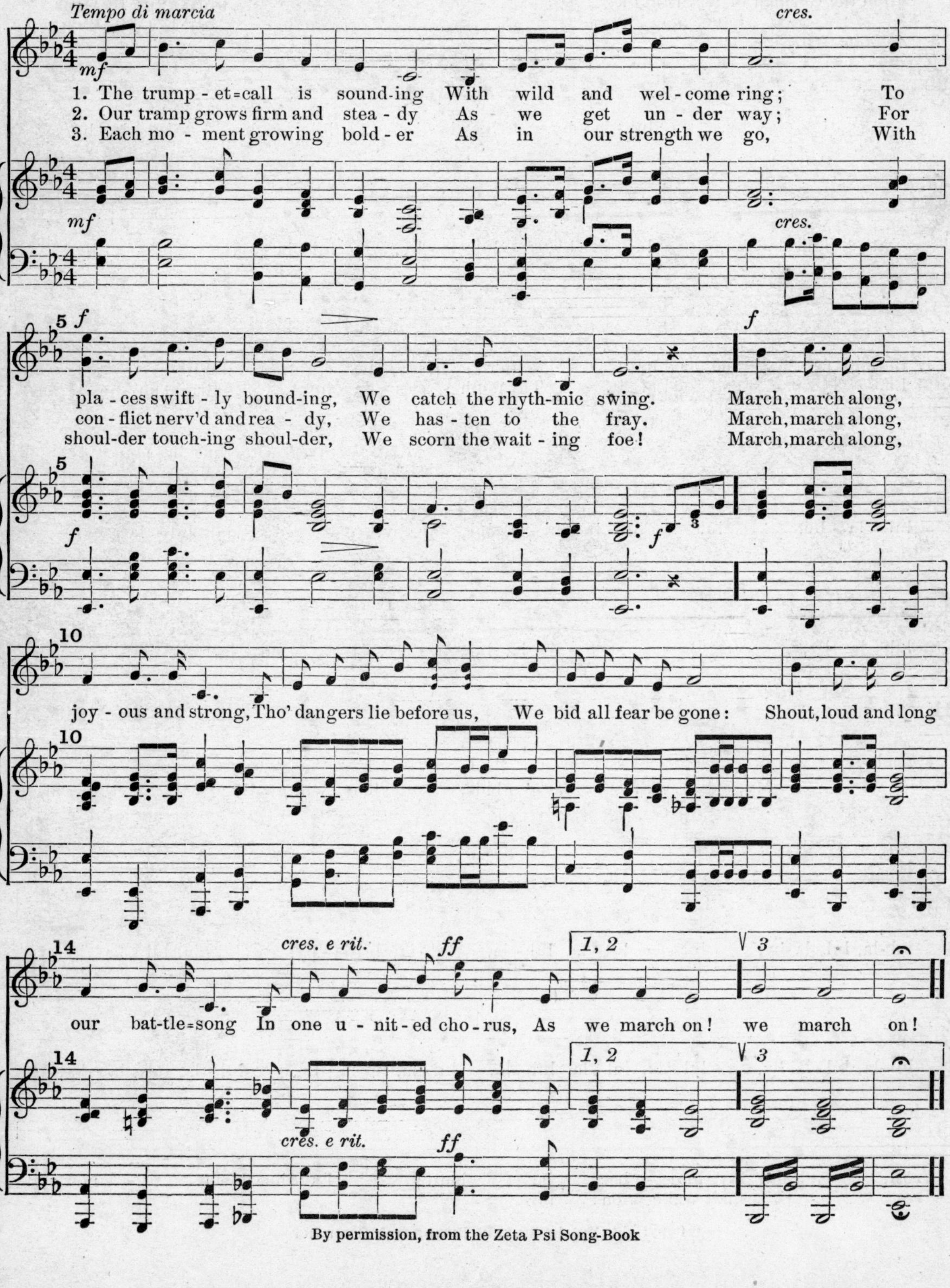

Tempo di marcia
mf
cres.
1. The trump - et=call is sound-ing With wild and wel - come ring; To
2. Our tramp grows firm and stea - dy As we get un - der way; For
3. Each mo - ment growing bold - er As in our strength we go, With
5
f
pla - ces swift - ly bound-ing, We catch the rhyth-mic swing. March, march along,
con - flict nerv'd and rea - dy, We has - ten to the fray. March, march along,
shoul-der touch-ing shoul-der, We scorn the wait - ing foe! March, march along,
10
joy - ous and strong, Tho' dangers lie before us, We bid all fear be gone: Shout, loud and long
14
cres. e rit.
ff
our bat-tle=song In one u - nit - ed cho - rus, As we march on! we march on!
1, 2
3

By permission, from the Zeta Psi Song-Book

Lullaby

Three-Part Song, with Melody in the Bass

From the German of K. Simrock

Johannes Brahms
Arr. by C. B. Rich

Copyright, 1909, by Silver, Burdett & Company

lul - la - by, lul - la, lul - la, lul - la, lul - la - by. lul - la, lul - la, lul - la,

lul - la - by, lul - la, lul - la, lul - la - by. lul - la, lul - la, lul - la,

rest, May thy slum - ber be blest. breast; They will

lul - la, lul - la - by, lul - la, lul - la - by, lul - la, lul - la, lul - la, lul - la, lul - la - by.

lul - la, lul - la - by, lul - la, lul - la - by, lul - la, lul - la - by, lul - la, lul - la - by.

guard thee at rest, Thou shalt wake on my breast.

Morning

Chorale in Four Parts

WILLIAM M. SAMPSON

From "The Pirates of Penzance"
ARTHUR SULLIVAN

1. Hail! shin-ing one! Au - ro - ra fair! The ro - sy mist en -crowns thy hair. Hail!
2. Hail! shin-ing one! Whose ra - diant face With glo - ry fills the am - bient space. Hail!

god-dess of the dew - y dawn; All hail! All hail! An - oth - er day is born!
god-dess of the blush-ing morn! All hail! All hail! An - oth - er day is born!

I Chose a Star in Heaven

For Four-Part Chorus

HOFFMANN VON FALLERSLEBEN

JOHN W. TUFTS

Andante tranquillo

1. I chose a star in heav - en, My guid - ing star to be, . . And
2. It was my guide so faith - ful, In man - y a gloom - y night, . And

oft as I looked thith - er, It bright - ly shone on me. . .
oft through un - seen dan - gers Led all my steps a - right. . .

The Shipwright

Unison Song for Low Voices

F. E. WEATHERLY

J. L. MOLLOY

Allegro moderato

Con spirito

1. The morn - ing breez - es gay - ly sing, The
2. The work is done, the skies are blue, The

sun is on the tide, A thou - sand ham - mers fall and ring A - cross the dock yard
wind blows fresh and gay— Then cut the strain - ing ropes in two And dash the shores* a-

* Props or beams. Ped.

The Faithful Echo

Three-Part Song for Equal Voices, with Optional Bass

Henry Hersee

Wilhelm Ganz

1. Through the val - ley, soon as morn Its wreath of gold - en sun - light brings,
2. Oft have lov - ers tried to gain A smile from Lil - la's laugh - ing eyes,

A song is on the breeze up-borne, 'Tis Lil - la's voice, and thus she sings: "My
But all their plead - ings are in vain; She still in mer - ry song re - plies: "I

joy - ous heart is free from care, And thus in care - less, hap - py strain, I
call on Ech - o to re - ply, For that can ne'er de - ceive you know." Then

wel - come in the morn - ing fair, I wel - come in the morn - ing fair, While
laugh - ter spark - les in her eye, Then laugh - ter spark - les in her eye, While

ech - o, ech - o, While ech - o, ech - o, while ech - o an - swers back a - gain."
ech - o, ech - o, While ech - o, ech - o, while faith - ful ech - o an - swers "No."

*Small note for use when Bass is sung.

Vacation Song

Three-part or Four-part Song (Optional Bass)

NORMAN D. SHERWOOD

KARL FRIEDRICH ZOLLNER

Spring Song

Three-Part Song for Soprano, Alto and Bass

Thornton W. Standish

Ferd. Gumbert

Copyright, 1909, by Silver, Burdett & Company

The Venetian Gondolier

NIXON WATERMAN

HENRY HADLEY

1. Joy - ful - ly the gon - do - lier Guides his hap - py boat, . . Glid - ing o'er the
2. Up and down her Grand Ca - nal, 'Mid her world of boats, . . In a ga - la
3. When at night the moon and stars Crown the skies a - bove, . . Then the notes of

1. Joy - ful - ly* the gon - do - lier Guides his boat, his hap - py boat, Glid - ing o'er the
2. Up and down her Grand Ca - nal, 'Mid her world of boats, of boats, In a ga - la
3. When at night the moon and stars Crown the skies a - bove, a - bove, Then the notes of

Guides his hap - py boat, . .
'Mid her world of boats, . .
Crown the skies a - bove, . .

wa - ters clear, Like a swan a - float. Thread-ing ma - ny a shin-ing way
fes - ti - val, Love - ly Ven - ice floats. Through her wind - ings, far and near,
soft gui - tars Tell of life and love. Mov - ing gay - ly to and fro,

wa - ters clear, Like a swan a - float. Thread - ing a shin - ing way
fes - ti - val Love - ly Ven - ice floats. Through her wind - ings, far and near,
soft gui - tars Tell of life and love. Mov - ing gay - ly to and fro,

* Alto-tenors prominent.

Copyright, 1909, by SILVER, BURDETT & COMPANY

A Forest Ramble

Three-Part Song for Equal Voices

EDWARD CORNWALL

FRANZ ABT

1. The day-star is shin-ing o'er moun-tain and lake,—The birds of the for-est from slum-ber a-wake, The dews hang like pearl drops on wild rose and thorn, All na-ture re-joic-es to wel-come the morn, All na-ture re-joic-es to wel-come the morn. Tra la, la, la, la, la, la, la, Tra la, la, la, la, la, la, la, . All na-ture re-joic-es to wel-come the morn.

2. As thus thro' the green-wood we wan-der a-long, And hear the wild lin-net,—me-lo-dious with song, We seem in its free-dom and glad-ness to share; Our hearts are un-burd-en'd of sor-row and care, Our hearts are un-burd-en'd of sor-row and care. Tra la, la, la, la, la, la, la, Tra la, la, la, la, la, la, la, . Our hearts are un-burd-en'd of sor-row and care.

3. The world's bright-est treas-ures soon van-ish and cloy, Com-pared with the pleas-ures like these we en-joy, They soothe and they cheer us, and light-en life's hours; Then wel-come the song=birds, the green-wood and bow'rs,Then wel-come the song=birds, the green-wood and bow'rs. Tra la, la, la, la, la, la, la, Tra la, la, la, la, la, la, la, . Then wel-come the song = birds, the green-wood and bow'rs.

Football Song

David K. Stevens

Arthur Sullivan

1. Let ev-'ry voice tri - umphant ring, We have
2. 'Tis a thrilling sight when the teams line up, And a-
3. O sing the game of the autumn field, When the

made the foe-man yield; We have won the day, By the gal - lant play Of our
wait the first at - tack; From the struggling mass Comes a for- ward pass, Or a
frost is in the air, When friend - ly strife is the joy of life, In a

lads on the white-barred field. For our col - ors now, a - bove them all, Float
kick of the quar - ter - back. A clev - er catch—a breath - less run, And a
sport be - yond com-pare! And give a cheer to the pluck - y foe, Who

Copyright, 1909, by Silver, Burdett & Company

proud-ly on the air; They're first to-day, And come what may, We're bound to keep them there!
hard-fought touch-down made; We're safe to-day, For that's the way The glo - ri - ous game is played!
fought the good fight thro'; It's all the same, For he plays the game — Three cheers and a ti-ger too!

O!.. for the day is done, The vic-t'ry won, And now for a rous - ing

cheer! It's three times three,'Till the ech - oes free, Are ring-ing far and near. Give a

Football Song

right - down reg - u - lar, reg - u - lar, reg - u - lar, Reg - u - lar rous - ing cheer!

cheer! It's three times three, 'Till the ech - oes free Are ring - ing, ring - ing

far and near, A right - down reg - u - lar rous - ing rah! hur - rah! . .

(Bass above Tenor)

Toward the Shores of Pellestrina*

Two-Part Song, with Optional Humming Accompaniment

From "The Tales of Hoffmann"

DAVID K. STEVENS

JACQUES OFFENBACH

1. Toward the shores of Pel - les-tri - na, boat-man, row a -
2. Toward the shores of Pel - les-tri - na, boat-man, row a -

way, . . Twink-ling lights in friendly win - dows gleam a-cross the bay.
way, . . Let our barque go leap-ing light - ly o'er the flash - ing spray.

In the vel - vet sky a-bove a mil - lion stars are bright, . . Shin - ing there like
Sing, un-til the wea - ry cares of day have tak - en flight, . . Sing of gen - tly

* Pellestrina is a beautiful island a few miles out from Venice. From this point a fine view of the Bay of Venice can be obtained. Near by is the island of Lido, where Byron wrote many of his works.

Copyright, 1909, by SILVER, BURDETT & COMPANY

There's Music in the Air

Three-Part Song, with Melody in Different Voices

George F. Root
Arr. by C. B. Rich

1. There's mu-sic in the air.. When the in-fant morn is nigh, And faint its blush is seen On the bright and laugh-ing sky. Ma-ny a harp's ec-sta-tic sound Thrills us with a joy pro-found, While we list, en-chant-ed there, To the mu-sic in the air.

2. There's mu-sic in the air, When noontide's

2. There's mu-sic in the air,

2. There's mu-sic in the air, ... When the noon-tide's sul-try

The Woodland Stream

Three-Part Song for Equal Voices

CHARLES MACKAY   W. T. WRIGHTON

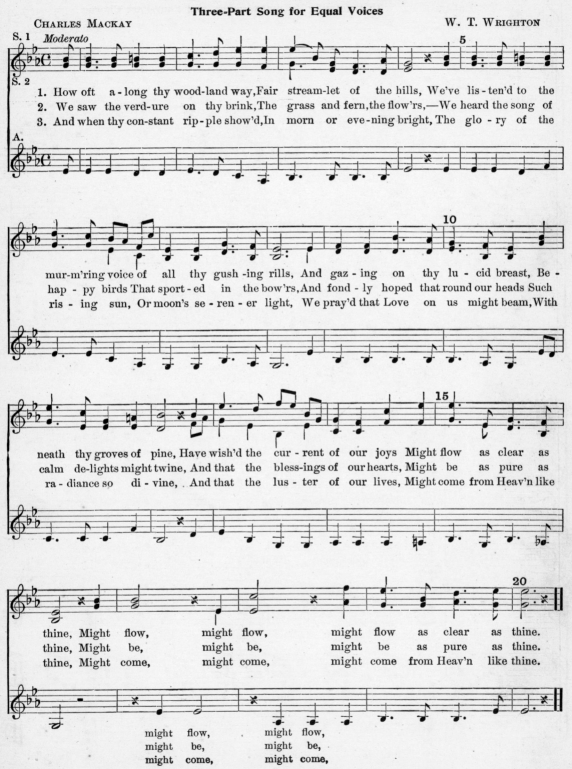

1. How oft a-long thy wood-land way, Fair stream-let of the hills, We've lis-ten'd to the mur-m'ring voice of all thy gush-ing rills, And gaz-ing on thy lu-cid breast, Be-neath thy groves of pine, Have wish'd the cur-rent of our joys Might flow as clear as thine, Might flow, might flow, might flow as clear as thine.

2. We saw the verd-ure on thy brink, The grass and fern, the flow'rs,—We heard the song of hap-py birds That sport-ed in the bow'rs, And fond-ly hoped that round our heads Such calm de-lights might twine, And that the bless-ings of our hearts, Might be as pure as thine, Might be, might be, might be as pure as thine.

3. And when thy con-stant rip-ple show'd, In morn or eve-ning bright, The glo-ry of the ris-ing sun, Or moon's se-ren-er light, We pray'd that Love on us might beam, With ra-diance so di-vine, And that the lus-ter of our lives, Might come from Heav'n like thine, Might come, might come, might come from Heav'n like thine.

might flow, might flow,
might be, might be,
might come, might come,

The Dance of the Fairies

Unison Song, with Humming Accompaniment, and Four-Part Chorus

Maurice K. Talbot

Louis Gregh

1. Soft-ly the woodland is dream - ing, Wrapped in the mantle of night:
2. Now the sad nightin-gale sing - ing, Tells her sweet grief to the moon,

Stars in the heav-ens are gleam - ing, Cheer-ing the earth with their light.
While the soft fair-y bells ring - ing, Bright-en the vales with their tune.

Here 'neath the moon as it tar - ries, Shed-ding its mel-low-est ray,
When the new morn-ing shall ban - ish Night with her ros-e-ate gleam,

The Dance of the Fairies

Glee-ful-ly gath-er the fair - ies, Danc-ing the mo-ments a-way. Gay-ly
Then the gay fair-ies shall van - ish Soft-ly a-way like a dream. Gay-ly

dance here in the moonlight so fair; Light as the air, Nev-er a care; While the
dance in the moon-light fair; Light as air, . . . While
dance in the moon-light fair; Light . . as air, . . . While

A Summer Evening

Three=Part Song for Equal Voices

David K. Stevens

Thomas Koschat

Slow - ly sinks be - hind a gold - en
As he slow - ly wings his loft - y
When the heart is filled with qui - et

1. Now the day is done, And the sum - mer sun Sinks be - hind a
2. In the pur - ple sky Sounds the night-hawk's cry, As he wings his
3. With the eve-ning chime, Comes the pen - sive time When the heart is

cloud; And the eve - ning shades Creep from dusk - y glades, Wrap - ping
flight; O'er the dis - tant marsh Comes the ac - cent harsh Of the
calm; And the gen - tle breeze, Through the whis - p'ring trees, Seems to

all the scene in som - bre shroud. Peace, with wing out-spread, Is hov - 'ring
her - on call - ing to the night. From the wood - land still, The cry of
soothe us like a heal - ing balm. Then, at Na - ture's shrine We plead for

The wea - ry toil - er rests con - tent;
Is min - gled with the night - birds' tune;
To guide us through the com - ing day;

o - ver-head; The wea - ry toil - er seeks his rest con - tent; Now his
whip - poor-will Is min - gled with the night-birds' plain-tive tune; While a -
love di - vine To guide us safe - ly through the com - ing day; Though it

The wea - ry toil - er rests con - tent;
Is min - gled with the night - birds' tune;
To guide us through the com - ing day;

Copyright, 1909, by Silver, Burdett & Company

A Summer Evening

task is done, A night's re-pose is won, At last the long and fruit-ful day is spent.
loft there gleams The light of sil-v'ry beams, Where shines the glory of the cres-cent moon.
well may be The path we can-not see, God's ten-der hand will lead us all the way.

My Normandy

Three=Part Song for Equal Voices

J. Annie Bense

Frédéric Bérat

1. How fair thy hills and wood-land ways, My Nor-man-dy, my Nor-man-dy!
   On pur-pling heights the sun-light plays, My Nor-man-dy, my Nor-man-dy!
2. On thee a-gain I fain would gaze, My Nor-man-dy, my Nor-man-dy!
   I hold thee as in oth-er days, My Nor-man-dy, my Nor-man-dy!
3. And when the gold of sun-light dies, My Nor-man-dy, my Nor-man-dy!
   And si-lent bend the star-ry skies, My Nor-man-dy, my Nor-man-dy!

Thy flow-'ry slopes, a foam-fleck'd sea, Thy wid-'ning wa-ters, flow-ing free,
And laugh-ing brook and wav-ing tree, Whose shad-ows trace the vel-vet lea,
In dreams thy dew-y vale I see, While ten-der mem-'ries call to me,

Hold all of life and love for me, My Nor-man-dy, my Nor-man-dy!
Still call my spir-it home to thee, My Nor-man-dy, my Nor-man-dy!
And wak-ing, lift my voice to thee, My Nor-man-dy, my Nor-man-dy!

Copyright, 1909, by SILVER, BURDETT & COMPANY

Bonnie Doon

Three-Part Song, with Melody in the Bass

ROBERT BURNS, adapted

Scotch Folksong
Arr. by C. B. RICH

S. *Allegretto*

1. Ye banks and braes* o' bon-nie Doon, How can ye bloom sae fair? . . . How
2. Oft hae I rov'd by bon-nie Doon, To see the wood-bine twine, . . . To

A.

1. Ye banks and braes* o' bon-nie Doon, How can ye bloom sae fresh and fair? How
2. Oft hae I rov'd by bon-nie Doon, To see the rose and woodbine twine, To

B.

1. Ye banks and braes* o' bon-nie Doon, How can ye bloom sae fresh and fair? How
2. Oft hae I rov'd by bon-nie Doon, To see the rose and woodbine twine, To

can ye chant, . . ye lit-tle birds, . . And I sae fu' o' care? . .
hear the birds . . sing o' their loves, . . As once I sang o' mine. . .

poco rit.

can ye chant, ye lit-tle birds, And I sae wea-ry, fu' o' care? . .
hear the birds sing o' their loves, As fond-ly once I sang o' mine. . .

poco rit. mf

can ye chant, ye lit-tle birds, And I sae wea-ry, fu' o' care? Thou'lt
hear the birds sing o' their loves, As fond-ly once I sang o' mine. Wi'

mf

Thou bon-nie bird, That sings up-on the flow-'ry thorn, Thou
I stretch'd my hand, And pu'd a rose-bud from the tree; But

rit. e dim. p

That sings up-on the flow-'ry thorn, Thou
And pu'd a rose-bud from the tree; But

rit. e dim. p

break my heart, thou bon-nie bird, That sings up-on the flow-'ry thorn, Thou
light-some heart I stretch'd my hand, And pu'd a rose-bud from the tree; But

* Hill-slopes.

a tempo moderato　　　　　　　　　15　　　*rit.*

'mindst me o' de - part - ed joys, De - part - ed nev - er to re - turn. . . .
my fause* lov - er stole my rose, And, ah! he left the thorn wi' me! . . . .

a tempo moderato　　　　　　　　　*rit.*

'mindst me o' de - part - ed joys, De - part - ed ne'er to re - turn. . . .
my fause* lov - er stole my rose, And left the thorn wi'. . . me! . . . .

a tempo moderato　　　　　　　　　*rit.*

'mindst me o' de - part - ed joys, De - part - ed nev - er to re - turn.
my fause* lov - er stole my rose, And, ah! he left the thorn wi' me!

* false.

The Mountain Brook
Three=Part Song for Equal Voices

Nixon Waterman

Franz Abt

Allegretto, molto grazioso

5 *cres.*

1. Slip - ping, slid - ing, danc - ing, glid - ing, Goes the brook, so . .
2. Glanc - ing, gleam - ing, bab - bling, beam - ing, Till with - in the .
3. Croon - ing, curl - ing, spark - ling, whirl - ing, Call - ing, mur - m'ring
4. Rush - ing, creep - ing, laugh - ing, leap - ing, Flows the brook by . .

mf *cres.*

poco dim. 10 *f*

glad and . gay: Where the sun's bright beams a - bid - ing Fleck with
qui - et . . pool, 'Neath the wil - low branch - es dream - ing Rests the
all day . long; Foam - ing, swirl - ing, play - ing, purl - ing, Sings the
lane and . lea, Till it joins the riv - er sweep - ing Ev - er

poco dim. *f*

15 *f* 20

gold . . the shin - ing way, Fleck with gold . . the shin - ing way.
brook . so calm and cool, Rests the brook . so calm and cool.
brook its mer - ry song, Sings the brook . its mer - ry song.
on - ward to the sea, Ev - er on - ward to the sea.

f

Copyright, 1909, by Silver, Burdett & Company

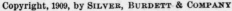

Waiting for the Maytime

Three-Part Song for Equal Voices

David Kilburn Stevens   Felix Mendelssohn-Bartholdy

Assai sostenuto

1. Ea - ger hearts im - pa - tient beat, Wait - ing for the May - time;
2. Win - ter wanes and grim - ly dies, Soon will come the May - time;
3. A - pril rain will wash the earth, Then will come the May - time;

Wait - ing for the sigh - ing breeze That whis - pers low a - mong the trees; O
Li - lac bring, and gold - en bell, Sweet mig - non - ette and as - pho - del, O
Fair and fresh the rose will bloom, The li - ly shed its sweet per - fume And

hap - py is the May - time, Fra - grant, balm - y May - time.
soon will come the May - time, Fra - grant, balm - y May - time.
blithe - ly deck the May - time, Fra - grant, balm - y May - time.

The Shepherd Lad

Three-Part Song for Equal Voices

Nixon Waterman   Carl Hering (Hungarian)

Vivo e leggiero

1. When the ro - sy morn a - wakes, Light-ing plain and moun - tain, Then I take my
2. When the gold - en sun of noon High a - bove is shin - ing, Then up - on my
3. When at eve a - down the west Goes the sun a = creep - ing, Then I blow my
4. When the stars of eve - ning shine In a count - less num - ber, Then my mel - low

pipe and call Beasts and bird - ies, one and all, To the crys - tal
pipe I blow Just to let the bird - ies know 'Tis the hour for
pipe un - til All the lit - tle birds are still In their nests a -
pipes I play Till at last I drift a - way In - to dream-less

foun - tain. Ha, Ha, Ha! I call them all To the crys - tal foun - tain.
din - ing. Ha, Ha, Ha! I let them know 'Tis the hour for din - ing.
sleep - ing. Ha, Ha, Ha! the birds are still, In their nests a = sleep - ing.
slum - ber. Ha, Ha, Ha! I drift a - way, In - to dream-less slum - ber.

Praise to God, Immortal Praise

For Four-Part Chorus

ANNA L. BARBAULD

L. M. GOTTSCHALK

Andante espressivo

1. Praise to God, im - mor - tal praise, For the love that crowns our days!
2. For the bless - ings of the field, For the stores the gar - dens yield,
3. All that Spring, with boun - teous hand Scat - ters o'er the smil - ing land;
4. These, to Thee, O God, we owe, Source whence all our bless - ings flow;

Boun - teous Source of ev - 'ry joy, Let Thy praise our tongues em - ploy!
For the fruits in full sup - ply, Rip - ened 'neath the sum - mer sky;
All that lib - 'ral Au - tumn pours From her o - ver - flow - ing stores;
And for these my soul shall raise Grate - ful vows and sol - emn praise.

The Carnival of Venice

Three-part or Four-part Song (Optional Bass)

HENRY F. SOUTHWORTH

Italian Melody

1. O fount of pur-est pleas-ure, O mel-low, mer-ry
2. With spir-its blithe and cheer-y, In hap-py voi-ces
3. With pag-eants all = en-tranc-ing; With wav-ing ban-ners

round, In rich-est, full-est meas-ure, Of joy-ous sight and sound! Gay
troll Thy gon-do-liers, so mer-ry, Their lilt-ing bar-ca-role. 'Neath
bright; With mu-sic, mirth, and danc-ing; With games by day and night; So

Copyright, 1909, by SILVER, BURDETT AND COMPANY

A Fairy Voyage

Two-Part Song for Equal Voices

KATE LOUISE BROWN

H. WALMSLEY LITTLE

1. O'er an el-fin sea   I glide,   Cra-dled by   its sil-ver tide,   On a
2. Fair-y hands un-furl   the sail,   Swell-ing to   a fair-y gale;   Fair-y
3. Care and sor-row flee   a-way,   Vis-ions of   an earth-born day—   Joy and

fair-y   sea   we roam,   Far from sail   or light of home.   Far from
fin-gers guide   the prow,   Fair-y fac-es crowd the bow.   Fair-y
mirth our guests shall be,   Laughing as   this sil-ver sea.   Laugh-ing

sail   or light of home.   In   the west the eve-ning star,   Smiles a-bove the
fac-es crowd the bow.   Jack   O'-Lan-tern   at the mast,   Shall proclaim the
as   this sil-ver sea.   Come with us   and blithe-ly roam,   Far from light or

cloud - land bar,   While the moon laughs down to   see   Such   a joy - ous
voy - age past,   When we gain the is - lands blest   Sleep - ing in the
sail of home.   Come, where waits the fair - y   rest   In   the pur - ple

rev - el - ry,   While the moon laughs down to   see Such a   joy - ous rev - el - ry.
pur - ple west,   When   we gain the   is - lands blest Sleep-ing in   the pur - ple west.
is - lands blest.   Come, where waits the   fair - y   rest, In the pur - ple is - lands blest.

A Moonlight Sail

Three-Part or Four-Part Song (Optional Bass)

DAVID K. STEVENS   From "Lucrezia Borgia," G. DONIZETTI

S. 1 *Allegro vivace*

1. Light - ly dancing o - ver the sea, In   our   shallop   rid - ing free; Moon-beams
2. From the hills a - long   the shore Sound the ech-oes o'er and o'er,   As   we

1. Light - ly danc-ing o - ver the sea, In   our   shal-lop   rid - ing free;   Moon-beams
2. From the hills a - long   the shore Sound the ech - oes o'er and o'er,   As   we

OP. B.

1. Light - ly danc-ing o - ver the sea, In   our   shal-lop   rid - ing free; Moon-beams
2. From the hills a - long   the shore Sound the ech - oes o'er and o'er,   As   we

A Moonlight Sail

rid - ing free, Rid-ing free, . . . rid-ing free, . . . O'er the sea, . . . While the
o'er and o'er, O'er and o'er, . . . o'er and o'er, . . . From the shore, . . . As we

rid - ing free, Rid-ing free, rid - ing free, O'er the sea,
o'er and o'er, O'er and o'er, o'er and o'er, From the shore,

rid - ing free, Rid - ing free, rid - ing free, O'er the sea,
o'er and o'er, O'er and o'er, o'er and o'er, From the shore,

moonbeams are soft - ly light-ing our way, Mak - ing gems, sparkling gems of the fly - ing
gay - ly, gay - ly glid-ing a - long, Wake the night, sleep-ing night, with our hap - py

Moon - beams soft - ly light-ing our way, Mak - ing gems, sparkling gems of the fly - ing
As we gay - ly glid-ing a - long, Wake the night, sleep-ing night, with our hap - py

Moon - beams soft - ly light-ing our way, Mak - ing gems, sparkling gems of the fly - ing
As we gay - ly glid-ing a - long, Wake the night, sleep-ing night, with our hap - py

spray, Mak - ing gems, sparkling gems of the fly - ing spray, of the fly - ing spray.
song, Wake the night, sleep-ing night, with our hap - py song, with our hap - py song.

spray, Mak - ing gems of the fly - ing spray, of the fly - ing spray.
song, Wake the night with our hap - py song, with our hap - py song.

spray, Mak - ing gems of the fly - ing spray, of the fly - ing spray.
song, Wake the night with our hap - py song, with our hap - py song.

Good Night

Two-Part Song for Equal Voices

NIXON WATERMAN

WILHELM TAUBERT

1. The gold is fad - ing from the west, The peace - ful world is wrapped in rest, The lit - tle stars their can - - - dles light. Now from the bus - y day's so - journ And all its wel - come

2. The wind is sleep - ing in the tree, And in her gold - en hive the bee Is rest - ing till the morn - ing bright. The flow - ers, as they drowse and dream A - mid the fra - grant

3. Now stilled are songs of lark and thrush, Yet on the eve - ning's tran - quil hush Come sounds our spir - its to . . . . in - vite. The cur - few bells in beau - ty toll As o'er the fields their

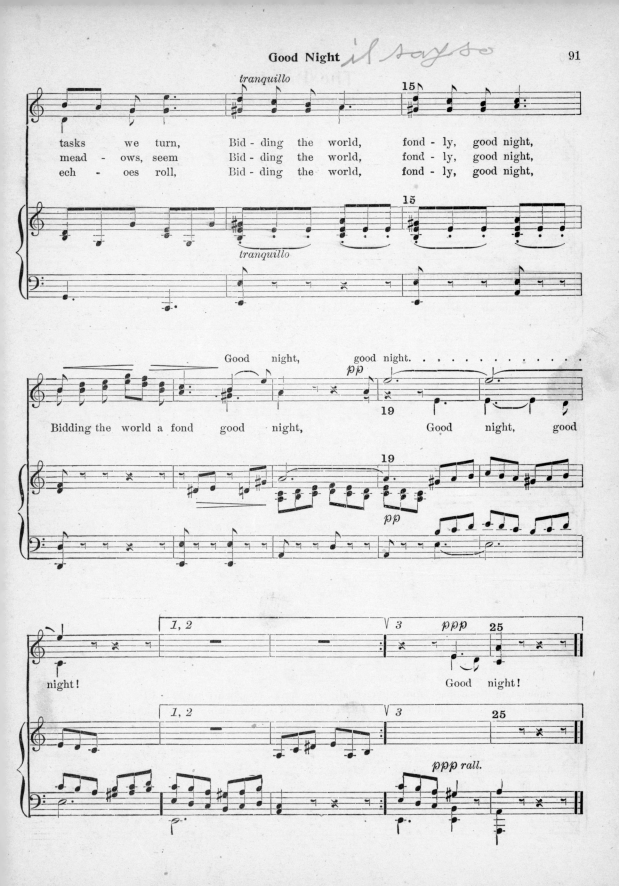

The Brook

Three-Part or Four-Part Song (Optional Bass)

J. Annie Bense

Franz Schubert

1. Swift glid-ing 'neath the beech - es On gleam-ing peb - ble white, Or curl-ing o'er the
2. It sweeps thro' fret-ted rock-way Be-neath a sky of blue, And high it flings its
3. The brook winds, gently steal-ing, A-fringe with i - ris fair, Bring-ing its grate-ful

1. Swift glid-ing 'neath the beech - es On gleam-ing peb - ble white, Or curl-ing o'er the
2. It sweeps thro' fret-ted rock-way Be-neath a sky of blue, And high it flings its
3. The brook winds, gently steal-ing, A-fringe with i - ris fair, Bring-ing its grate-ful

reach - es, In glanc-ing sun-shine bright, A brook slips, soft-ly sing-ing Of
foam=spray; Its song is ev - er new; It sings of ro - sy morn-ing, And
heal-ing To ev - 'ry blos-som rare. But now it sings no long-er Of

reach - es, In glanc-ing sun-shine bright, A brook slips, soft-ly sing-ing Of
foam=spray; Its song is ev - er new; It sings of ro - sy morn-ing, And
heal-ing To ev - 'ry blos-som rare. But now it sings no long-er Of

depths 'neath al - der shade, Where moss-es green are cling - ing, And shad - ows fleck the
moun-tain peaks a - glow, Of all the lights of dawn-ing When all the breez-es
moun-tain, glade and tree, Of nest and ti - ny song - ster, As, rush-ing to the

depths 'neath al - der shade, Where moss-es green are cling - ing, And shad - ows fleck the
moun-tain peaks a - glow, Of all the lights of dawn-ing When all the breez-es
moun-tain, glade and tree, Of nest and ti - ny song - ster, As, rush-ing to the

glade, And where the wild bird wing - ing Its ti - ny nest has made.
blow, When stars give pale their warn - ing, And bird - note wak - ens low.
sea, Its glad song ev - er strong - er, It swells its cho - rus free.

glade, And where the wild bird wing - ing Its ti - ny nest has made.
blow, When stars give pale their warn - ing, And bird - note wak - ens low.
sea, Its glad song ev - er strong - er, It swells its cho - rus free.

Kelvin Grove

Three-Part Song for Equal Voices

Scotch Folksong

Andante

1. Let us haste to Kel - vin Grove, bon - nie las - sie, O; Through its ma - zes let us
2. Let us wan - der by the mill, bon - nie las - sie, O; To the cove be - side the
3. O . . Kel - vin banks are fair, bon - nie las - sie, O; When the sum - mer we are

cres. *slower*

rove, bon - nie las - sie, O; Where the ro - ses in their pride Deck the
rill, bon - nie las - sie, O; Where the glens re - sound the call Of the
there, bon - nie las - sie, O; There the May - pinks' crim - son plume Throws a

dim. *a tempo* *rit.*

bon - nie din - gle = side, Where the mid - night fair - ies glide, bon - nie las - sie, O.
roar - ing wa - ter's fall, Through the moun - tain's rock - y hall, bon - nie las - sie, O.
soft but sweet per - fume, Round the yel - low banks o' broom, bon - nie las - sie, O.

Fairy Revelry

Three-Part or Four-Part Song (Optional Bass)

EDWARD PAYSON JACKSON

GIOACHINO ROSSINI

1. What soul=thrill - ing song=charm, like sweet sil - ver bells, Rings from yon star - lit
2. Their rai - ment trans - lu - cent, of light pearl - y hue, Shines in moon-light like

1. What soul=thrill - ing song=charm, like sweet sil - ver bells, Rings from yon star - lit
2. Their rai - ment trans - lu - cent, of light pearl - y hue, Shines in moon-light like

moor-land a - way down the dells? The fair queen of Elf-land has marshalled her
cob-webs be - spray'd o'er with dew. With elf - play and glee-song, so buoy-ant and

moor-land a - way down the dells? The fair queen of Elf-land has marshalled her
cob-webs be - spray'd o'er with dew, With elf - play and glee-song, so buoy-ant and

ring, And bids all the fair - ies to dis - port and sing; The fair queen of
gay, They dance till the dawn breaks and drives them a - way; With elf - play and

ring, And bids all the fair - ies to dis - port and sing; The fair queen of
gay, They dance till the dawn breaks and drives them a - way; With elf - play and

Elf - land has marshalled her ring, And bids all the fair - ies to
glee- song, so buoy - ant and gay, They dance till the dawn breaks and

Elf - land has marshalled her ring, And bids all the fair - ies to
glee- song, so buoy - ant and gay, They dance till the dawn breaks and

dis - port and sing; And bids all the fair - ies to dis - port and sing.
drives them a - way; They dance till the dawn breaks and drives them a - (Omit.)

dis - port and sing; And bids all the fair - ies to dis - port and sing.
drives them a - way; They dance till the dawn breaks and drives them a - (Omit.)

way. Yes, they dance till the dawn breaks and drives them a - way.

way. Yes, they dance till the dawn breaks and drives them a - way.

The Swan

Harvey Worthington Loomis

Richard Wagner in "Lohengrin"
Arr. by Harvey Worthington Loomis

1. Swan, swan, who knows thy song? Swan, swan, vis - ion
2. Swan, swan, who knows thy song? Swan, swan, form of

[Soprano II reads text with Tenor]

1. Swan, swan, who knows thy song? Swan, swan, vis - ion
2. Swan, swan, who knows thy song? Swan, swan, form of

bright!. O snow - y swan, Out of the si - lence float - - est thou Up -
light!. O spir - it pure, What charm - ed dawn = time brought thee forth? Thy

bright!.
light!.. E'er float, ...
E'er float, ...

Copyright, 1909, by Silver, Burdett & Company

Must thou re-main for-ev - er mute? Swan, swan, who knows thy song?
In-to the si - lence float-est thou! Swan, swan, who knows thy song?

Ev - - er float, . . . Swan, swan, who knows thy song?

. . float, ... Swan, . . swan, who knows thy song?

Float, . . . e'er float, ... Swan, swan, who knows thy song?

Old King Cole

Unison Song for Basses, with Two-Part Vocal Accompaniment

English Folksong, arr. by C. B. RICH

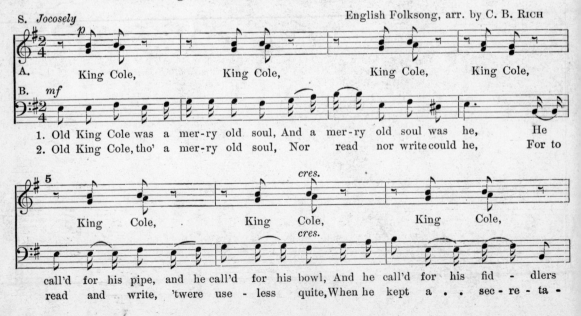

King Cole, King Cole, King Cole, King Cole,

1. Old King Cole was a mer-ry old soul, And a mer-ry old soul was he, He
2. Old King Cole, tho' a mer-ry old soul, Nor read nor write could he, For to

King Cole, . King Cole, King Cole,

call'd for his pipe, and he call'd for his bowl, And he call'd for his fid - dlers
read and write, 'twere use - less quite, When he kept a . . sec-re-ta-

The Spanish Gipsy

Unison Song for Medium or Low Voices

MICHAEL WATSON

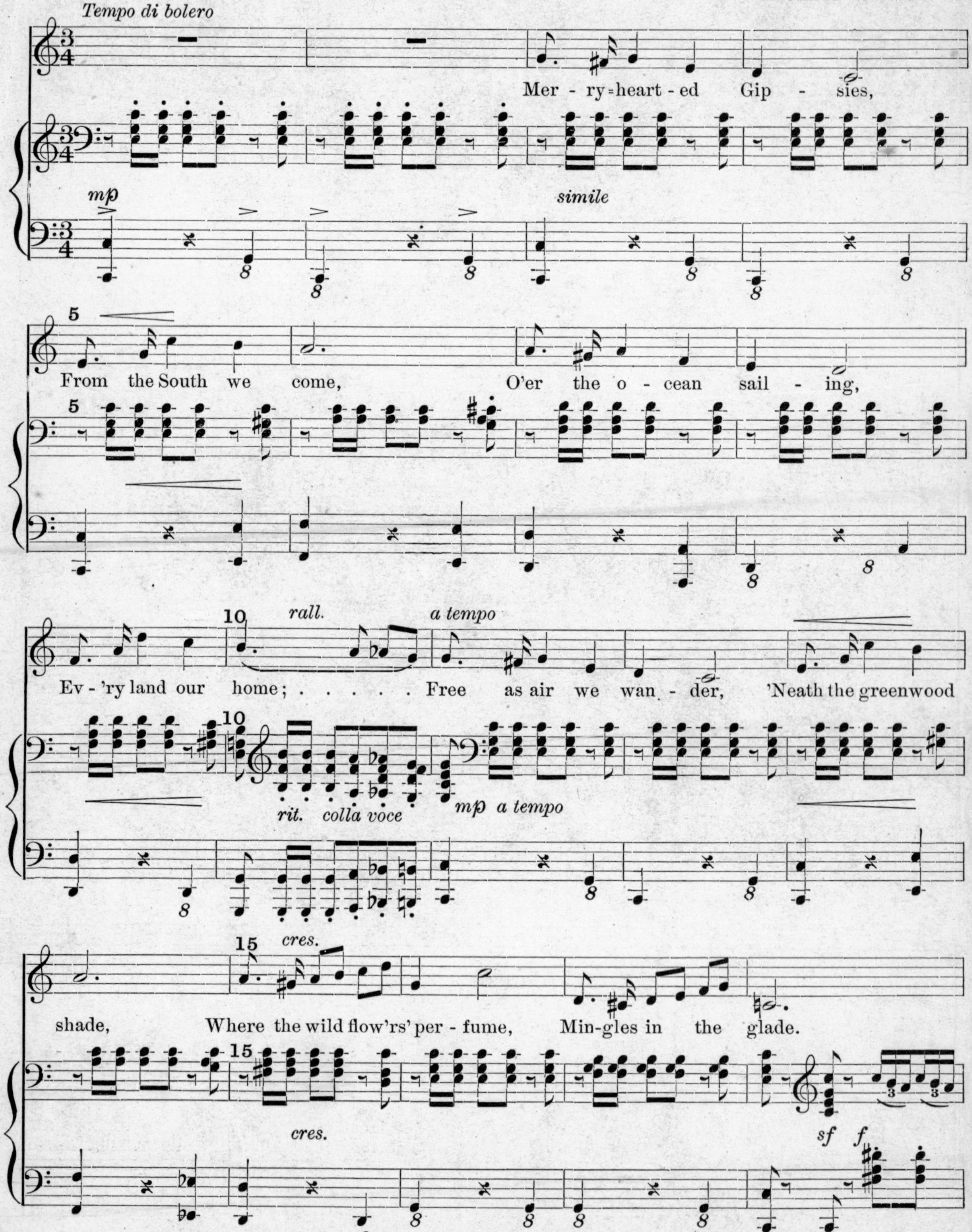
Tempo di bolero
Mer - ry-heart - ed Gip - sies,
mp
simile
5
From the South we come, O'er the o - cean sail - ing,
10
rall.
a tempo
Ev - 'ry land our home; . . . . . Free as air we wan - der, 'Neath the greenwood
rit. colla voce
mp a tempo
15
cres.
shade, Where the wild flow'rs' per - fume, Min-gles in the glade.
sf
f

For - tunes we tell as on - ward we .. roam, And Do - na or Don re - spond to .. our call; ...... "Greet - ing," they cry, "O daugh - ter of Spain" La

bel - la Gi - ta - na is   wel - - com'd by all.

Ho - la!   Ho - la! . . . .   Ho -

la! 'Tis the Gip - sy, who comes from Se - ville,   where or - ange and

cit - ron trees per - fume the grove.   Ho - la!   cross my

palm and I soon will re - veal, A tale that shall

breathe but of joy - bells and love.

Queen of Night

For Three-Part or Four-Part Chorus (Optional Bass)

DAVID K. STEVENS

ERIK MEYER–HELMUND, arr.

1. Eve-ning falls, the sun is sink-ing: At the pool the
2. Na-ture's chil-dren home are creep-ing, Bird-lings in their

hap - py dreams. Fair the sun that glows with golden light — Thou art

hap - py dreams. Fair the sun that glows with golden light — Thou art

hap - py dreams. Fair the sun that glows with golden light — Thou art

fair - er still, O Queen of night!

fair - er still, O Queen of night!

fair - er still, O Queen of night!

rit. pp

Regatta Song

Unison Song for Medium Voices, with Four-Part Chorus

David K. Stevens

Charles Fonteyn Manney

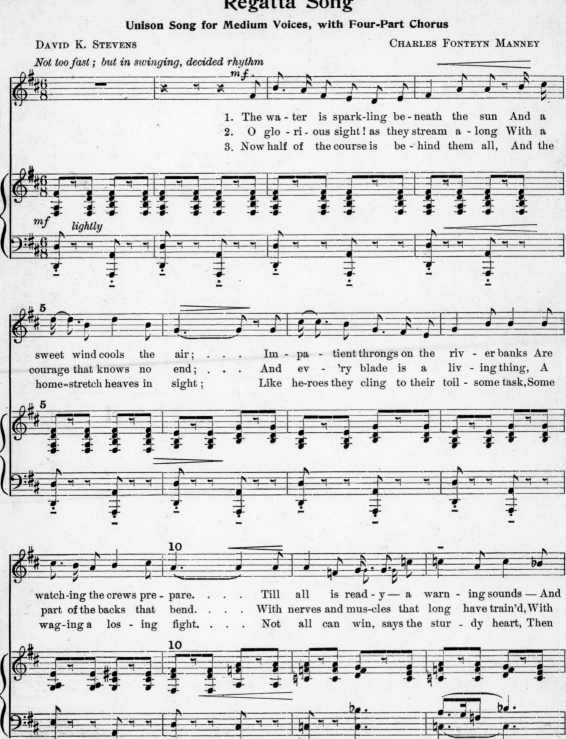

1. The wa - ter is spark-ling be - neath the sun And a
2. O glo - ri - ous sight! as they stream a - long With a
3. Now half of the course is be - hind them all, And the

sweet wind cools the air; ... Im - pa - tient throngs on the riv - er banks Are
courage that knows no end; ... And ev - 'ry blade is a liv - ing thing, A
home=stretch heaves in sight; Like he-roes they cling to their toil - some task, Some

watch-ing the crews pre - pare. .... Till all is read - y — a warn - ing sounds — And
part of the backs that bend. .... With nerves and mus-cles that long have train'd, With
wag-ing a los - ing fight. ... Not all can win, says the stur - dy heart, Then

Copyright, 1909, by SILVER, BURDETT & COMPANY

Regatta Song

ash - en blades are bend - ing now, And noth - ing our course can stay, . . For it's

ash - en blades are bend - ing now, And noth - ing our course can stay, . . For it's

ash - en blades are bend - ing now, And noth - ing our course can stay, . . For it's

swing, swing! stead - y, my boys, We are bound to win to - day! . .

swing, swing! stead - y, my boys, We are bound to win to - day! . .

swing, swing! stead - y, my boys, We are bound to win to - day! . .

Massa's in de Cold, Cold Ground

Unison Song for Basses, with Humming Accompaniment

S. C. Foster

S. C. Foster
Arr. by C. B. Rich

1. Round de mead-ows am a - ring - ing De dark - y's mourn - ful song,
2. When de au - tumn leaves were fall - ing, When de days were cold, 'Twas
3. Mas - sa make de dark - ies love him 'Cayse he was so kind;

While de mocking-birds am sing - ing, Hap - py as de day am long.
hard to hear old Mas - sa call - ing, 'Cayse he was so weak and old.
Now dey sad - ly weep a - bove him, Mourn - ing 'cayse he leave dem be - hind.

Where de i - vy am a creep - ing O'er de grass - y mound,
Now de or-ange=trees am bloom - ing On de sand - y shore,
I can't work be - fore to - mor - row, 'Cayse de tear - drops flow:

Copyright, 1909, by SILVER, BURDETT & COMPANY

Dar old Mas - sa am a = sleep - ing,   Sleeping in de cold, cold ground.
Now de sum-mer days am com - ing,   Mas - sa neb-ber calls no more.
try   to drive a - way my sor - row,   Pick-ing on de old ban - jo.

Mm . . . .

Mm . . . .

Down in de corn - field, Hear dat mourn-ful sound;   All   de dark-ies am a =

Mm . . . .

Mm . . . .

weep - ing; Mas-sa's in de cold, cold ground. . . . .   ground. . . . . .

Nymphs of Air and Sea

Three-Part Song for Equal Voices

HENRY SMART

1. Nymphs of air and an-cient sea, Such the gifts we bring to thee;
2. Take these shells, ap-proach them near; They shall mur-mur in thine ear,

Lo! these plumes of rich de-vice, Pluck'd from birds of Par-a-dise.
Tunes that lull the slum-b'ring sea, — More than mer — maid's har-mo-ny.

Lo! these plumes of rich de-vice, Pluck'd from birds of Par-a-dise.
Tunes that lull the slum-b'ring sea, More than mer-maid's har-mo-ny.

Lo! these drops of es-sence rare . . . . Flung from wand-'ring me-teor's
Take these pearls, no di-ving slave . . . Drags their like from o-cean's

Lo! these drops of es-sence rare,
Take these pearls, no div-ing slave

hair. Nymphs of air and an-cient sea,
cave. Nymphs of air and an-cient sea,

Flung from wand-ring me-teor's hair. Nymphs of an-cient sea, Such the gifts we bring to
Drags their like from o-cean's cave. Nymphs of an-cient sea, Such the gifts we bring to

thee; Nymphs of air and an-cient sea, Such the gifts we bring to thee.

The Shepherd's Good Night

Two-Part Song for Sopranos and Tenor-Altos

STUART MAY

From "Il Trovatore"

G. VERDI

Calm and se-rene now the day is end-ing,

Slow-ly the sun o'er the hill de-scend-ing; Shad-ows are fall-ing Deep 'neath the

trees; Night=birds are call-ing, Low sighs the breeze. Soft - ly the

bells dis-tant mel - o - dy lend, Pro-claim-ing the flocks as home - ward they

The Shepherd's Good Night

night, Good   night!" the maid- en is   cry - ing; "And may fair dreams thy slum-bers at -
night, Good   night!" the shep-herd re - ply - ing, "Thy rest from ill   may an - gels de -

"Good night, Fair dreams thy slum-bers at -
"Good night! From ill   may an - gels de -

tend. Good   night! Fair dreams   thy   rest at - tend. Good
(Omit . .) fend. Good night! From ill   an - gels de - (Omit . . .)

tend.   Fair dreams   thy rest   at - tend.
(Omit . .) fend.   From ill   an - gels   de -(Omit)

fend.   Good night, good night!   Good night,good   night." . . . .

fend.   Good night, good night!   Good night,good   night." . . . .

Old Folks at Home

Melody in the Bass, with Humming Accompaniment

S. C. FOSTER

S. C. FOSTER
Arr. by C. B. RICH

1. 'Way down up-on the Swa-nee Riv-er, Far, far a-
2. All 'round the lit-tle farm I wan-der'd, When I was
3. One lit-tle hut a-mong the bush-es, One that I

way, There's where my heart is turn-ing ev-er, There's where the old folks
young, Then ma-ny hap-py days I squan-der'd, Ma-ny the songs I
love, Still sad-ly to my mem-'ry rush-es, No mat-ter where I

stay. All up and down the whole cre-a-tion, Sad-ly I roam,
sung. When I was play-ing with my broth-er, Hap-py was I!
rove. When shall I see the bees a-hum-ming, All 'round the comb?

Copyright, 1909, by SILVER, BURDETT & COMPANY

Still long-ing for the old plan-ta-tion, And for the old folks at home.
O take me to my kind old moth-er, There let me live and die!
When shall I hear the ban - jo thrumming, Down in my good old home?

Mm

Mm

All the world is sad and drear-y Ev - 'ry-where I roam,

O dark - ies, how my heart grows wea-ry, Far from the old folks at home!

A Summer Holiday

For Four-Part Chorus, with Unisons or Solos

David K. Stevens

From "Iolanthe,"
Arthur Sullivan

1. The morn - ing sun is glow - ing bright, The
come! the morn - ing sun is high, The

cool and si - lent lanes in -vite, While up and down a moss - y path the
clouds are few and blue the sky, The sum - mer air is la - den with the

A Summer Holiday

cow - slip and the but - ter-cup are nodding in the sun; From ev - 'ry care and

trou - ble free, Our voic - es ring in mer - ry glee; The shin - ing hours are

all for us, The day is just be - gun! The day is just be - gun! The

shin - ing hours are all for us, The hap - py day is just be - gun! O

The Morn of the Year

Unison Song

Text and music by
HARVEY WORTHINGTON LOOMIS

Not too slowly

1. The sea - sons come and the sea - sons go, With shine . or rain, . Ar -
2. The sea - sons go and the sea - sons come To fill . . the year, . But

With gentle movement

bu - tus waits 'neath the win - ter's snow For spring . a - gain. .
birds will car - ol and bees will hum When spring . is here. .

Copyright, 1909, by SILVER, BURDETT & COMPANY

Meadow Song

CLINTON SCOLLARD

L. B. MARSHALL

Copyright, 1909, by SILVER, BURDETT & COMPANY

blue - - bells that bloom in the spring.... And the hue of the
blue - - bells that bloom in the spring..... With a sky brood-ing
blue - - bells that bloom in the spring..... With lus - tre - ful

cres.

fair as the blue - bells, bloom in the spring. And the hue of the
fair as the blue - bells, bloom in the spring. With a sky brood-ing
fair as the blue - bells, bloom in the spring. With lus - tre - ful

cres.

sky that leans lov - ing - ly o - ver, Is fair as the blue-bells that bloom in the spring.
o - ver as clear as clear glass is, And fair as the blue-bells that bloom in the spring.
sky lean-ing ten - der - ly o - ver, As fair as the blue-bells that bloom in the spring.

sky that leans lov - ing - ly o - ver, Is fair as the blue-bells that bloom in the spring.
o - ver as clear as clear glass is, And fair as the blue-bells that bloom in the spring.
sky lean-ing ten - der - ly o - ver, As fair as the blue-bells that bloom in the spring.

Song of Exaltation

OLIVER WENDELL HOLMES

LUDWIG VAN BEETHOVEN

Andante

1. Lord of our be - ing, throned a - far, Thy glo - ry flames from sun and star;
2. Sun of our life, thy quick'ning ray Sheds on our path the glow of day:
3. Grant us thy truth to make us free, And kind - ling hearts that burn for thee,

Cen - tre and soul of ev - 'ry sphere, Yet to each lov - ing heart how near.
Star of our hope, thy soft-ened light Cheers the long watch-es of the night.
Till all thy liv - ing al - tars claim One ho - ly light, one heav'n - ly flame.

The Song of the Swallow

Unison Song for Basses

Thornton W. Standish

Robert Radecke

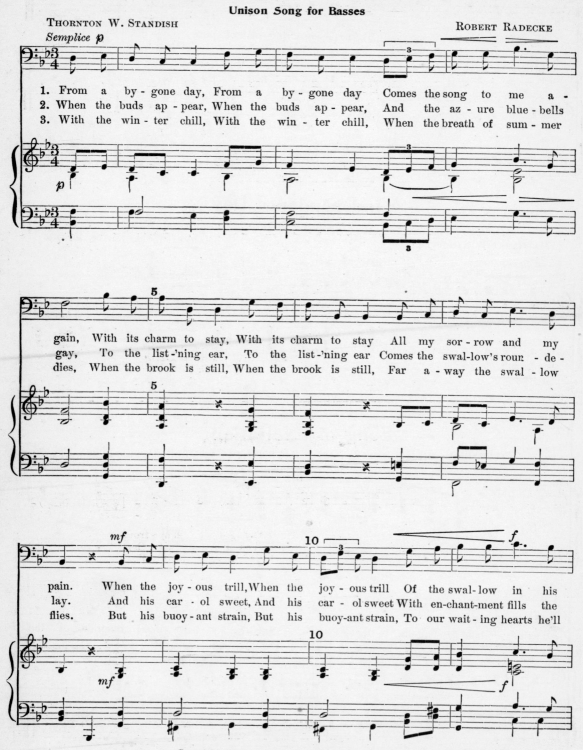

1. From a by-gone day, From a by-gone day Comes the song to me a-gain, With its charm to stay, With its charm to stay All my sor-row and my pain. When the joy-ous trill, When the joy-ous trill Of the swal-low in his
2. When the buds ap-pear, When the buds ap-pear, And the az-ure blue-bells gay, To the list-'ning ear, To the list-'ning ear Comes the swal-low's roun-de-lay. And his car-ol sweet, And his car-ol sweet With en-chant-ment fills the
3. With the win-ter chill, With the win-ter chill, When the breath of sum-mer dies, When the brook is still, When the brook is still, Far a-way the swal-low flies. But his buoy-ant strain, But his buoy-ant strain, To our wait-ing hearts he'll

Copyright, 1909, by Silver, Burdett & Company

The Song of the Swallow

flight, Wakes the answ'ring thrill, Wakes the answ'ring thrill of pure de - light.
air, Ev - 'ry note re - plete, Ev - 'ry note re-plete With prom - ise rare.
bring, He'll re - turn a - gain, He'll re - turn a - gain With (*Omit . . .*) blithesome Spring.

Independence Day
Unison Song

MARGARET E. SANGSTER

HARVEY WORTHINGTON LOOMIS

Beau - ti - ful coun - try, fair home of the free, Pine - land and

palm - land pay trib-ute to thee, Nev - er a ban - ner like thine of the

Copyright, 1909, by SILVER, BURDETT AND COMPANY
E

stars, . . . Nev-er a dis-cord thy mel - o - dy mars. Moth-er of

mil - lions, thy chil-dren to thee, . . . Hast-en with an - thems, fair home of the

free. Moth-er of mil - lions, thy chil-dren to thee . . Hast-en with

an - thems, fair home of the free ! . . . . Thun-der of can-non from fort and from

Land of the free! . . . . Up - ward thou

look - est to God and the right, Down-ward to cheer . . those who make the good

fight. . . Moth- er of mil - lions, from coast un - to coast, . . . Learn - ing and

lib - er - ty still . . are thy boast; Beau - ti - ful coun - try, great land of the

The Shepherd Boy

Alfred Tennyson

George B. Nevin

The Minuet

DAVID KILBURN STEVENS

HENRY HADLEY

1. In days when bro - cade Was the us - u - al wear, When gal - lants wore
2. And then down the mid - dle De - mure - ly they go, In step to the

1. In days when bro - cade Was the us - u - al wear, When gal - lants wore
2. And then down the mid - dle De - mure - ly they go, In step to the

1. In days when bro - cade Was the us - u - al wear, When gal - lants wore
2. And then down the mid - dle De - mure - ly they go, In step to the

small clothes And pow - dered their hair, 'Twas then, when at rout . . And as -
meas - ure So rhyth - mic and slow; An - oth - er o - bei - sance In . .

small clothes And pow - dered their hair, 'Twas then, when at rout And as -
meas - ure So rhyth - mic and slow; An o - bei - sance grand In . .

small clothes And pow - dered their hair, 'Twas then, . . . when at rout
meas - ure So rhyth - mic and slow; An o - bei - sance grand

The Village Festival

Nixon Waterman

Carrie Bullard

Copyright, 1909, by Silver, Burdett & Company

Evening Bells

Three-Part Song for Equal Voices

THOMAS MOORE

L. B. MARSHALL

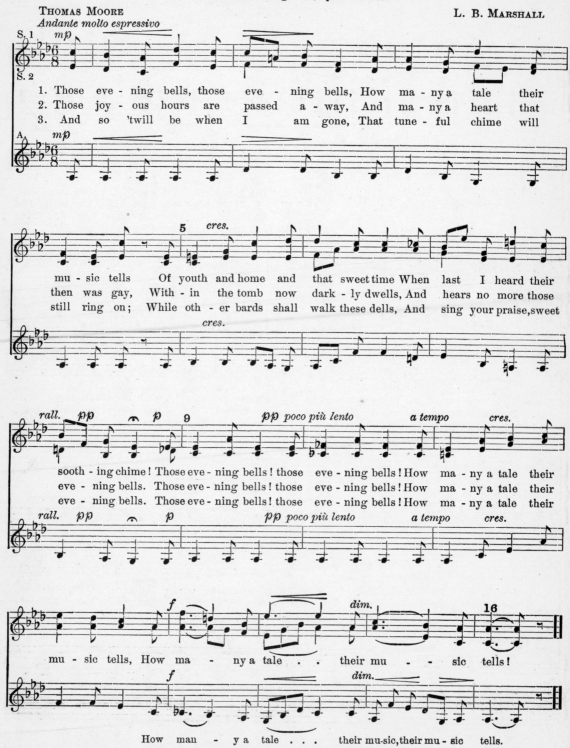

Andante molto espressivo

1. Those eve-ning bells, those eve-ning bells, How ma-ny a tale their mu-sic tells Of youth and home and that sweet time When last I heard their sooth-ing chime! Those eve-ning bells! those eve-ning bells! How ma-ny a tale their mu-sic tells, How ma-ny a tale . . their mu-sic tells!

2. Those joy-ous hours are passed a-way, And ma-ny a heart that then was gay, With-in the tomb now dark-ly dwells, And hears no more those eve-ning bells. Those eve-ning bells! those eve-ning bells! How ma-ny a tale their

3. And so 'twill be when I am gone, That tune-ful chime will still ring on; While oth-er bards shall walk these dells, And sing your praise, sweet eve-ning bells. Those eve-ning bells! those eve-ning bells! How ma-ny a tale their

How man-y a tale . . . their mu-sic, their mu-sic tells.

Basket=Ball Song

For Medium Voice, Unison Chorus, and Four-Part Chorus

David K. Stevens

Arthur Sullivan

Copyright, 1909, by Silver, Burdett & Company

Basket-Ball Song

Up and a-way, the ball is in play! The whis-tle sounds, so up and a-way! Hur-
Up and a-way, and keep it in play! 'Tis fly-ing back, so up and a-way! And
Up and a-way, the ball is in play! The sig-nal comes, so up and a-way! A-
Some oth-er day a-gain we will play! So give a cheer for some oth-er day, The

rah! the ball's in play! Hip, hip, hur-rah! Hip, hip, hur-rah! Hip, hip, hur-rah, hur-rah, hur-
keep the ball in play! Hip, hip, hur-rah! Hip, hip, hur-rah! Hip, hip, hur-rah, hur-rah, hur-
gain the ball's in play! Hip, hip, hur-rah! Hip, hip, hur-rah! Hip, hip, hur-rah, hur-rah, hur-
ball will be in play! Hip, hip, hur-rah! Hip, hip, hur-rah! Hip, hip, hur-rah, hur-rah, rah-

rah! . . So al-ways keep the ball in sight As you make it nim-bly

spin ; . . And hip, hur-rah! Hip, hip, hur-rah! Hip, hip, hip! hip, hur-

rah! . . . . . . For we play the game with all our might and play . . . .

to win. . . . . . .

By Starlight

Three-Part Song for Equal Voices, with Optional Bass

C. B. Rich

Franz Abt

S. 1 *Allegretto*

S. 2

1. Swan-like the shal-lops are roam - ing   O'er the shim-mer-ing lake;
2. Dain - ty shells, ra - diant-ly gleam - ing,   Mir - ror heav'n on the shore;
3. Here, a - mid fragrance and splen - dor,   Gemmed a - bove and a - round,

A.

1. Swan-like the shal-lops are roam - ing   O'er the shim-mer-ing lake; See! yon - der
2. Dain - ty shells, ra - diant-ly gleam - ing,   Mir - ror heav'n on the shore; Rich- ly, 'mid
3. Here, a - mid fragrance and splen - dor,   Gemmed a - bove and a - round, Praise un - to

Op. B.

5 *cres.*

See! yon-der star, thro' the gloam - ing,   Is scatt'ring its beams in their wake.
Rich - ly, 'mid ev - en-tide's dream - ing,   The flow-ers their fragrance out - pour.
Praise un - to Him let us ren - der   Who earth with such beau-ty has crowned.

cres.

star, . . thro' the gloam - ing,   Is scatt'ring its beams in their wake. Sing we our
ev - en - tide's dream - ing,   The flow-ers their fragrance out - pour. Sing we our
Him . . let . . us ren - der   Who earth with such beau-ty has crown'd. Sing we our

cres.

See! yon-der star, thro' the gloam - ing,
Rich - ly, 'mid ev - en-tide's dream - ing,
Praise un - to Him let us ren - der

f   10   *p*

Sing we our song of re - joic - ing, 'Mid Na - ture's calm re - pose,

p   *f*

song, our song of re - joic - ing 'Mid Na - ture's calm re - pose, Hum-bly our

f   *p*

Sing we our song of re - joic - ing, 'Mid Na - - - ture's calm re-pose,

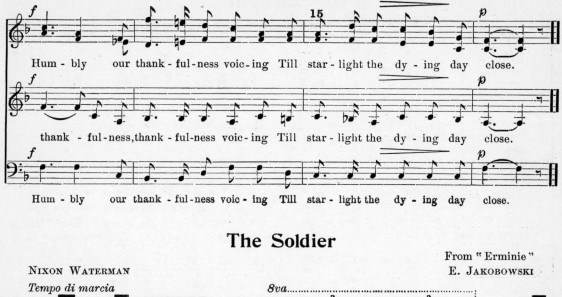

Hum - bly   our thank - ful - ness voic - ing Till star - light the dy - ing day   close.

thank - ful - ness, thank - ful - ness voic - ing Till star - light the dy - ing day   close.

Hum - bly   our thank - ful - ness voic - ing Till star - light the dy - ing day   close.

The Soldier

NIXON WATERMAN

From " Erminie "
E. JAKOBOWSKI

Tempo di marcia

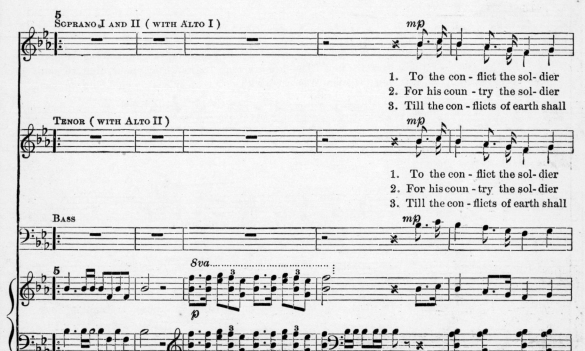

SOPRANO I AND II (WITH ALTO I)

1. To the con - flict the sol - dier
2. For his coun - try the sol - dier
3. Till the con - flicts of earth shall

TENOR (WITH ALTO II)

1. To the con - flict the sol - dier
2. For his coun - try the sol - dier
3. Till the con - flicts of earth shall

BASS

goes   With a   pur-pose ev - er strong and true ;   He fal - ters not   to   meet his foes, But
lives,   For his flag the val-iant soldier dies ;   His strength and zeal   he   glad - ly gives To
cease   From the strife the an-gels must abhor ;   Till Truth shall sit   en-throned in peace, Her

brave-ly   seeks to dare and do ;   And where glo - ry shall point the   way,   With a
keep   his ban-ner in the sky ;   Like the   stars   in the heav'n a - bove,   All its
foes shall still be scourged with war ;   And the   sol - dier with sword and   gun   'Neath his

cour - age scorn-ing ev - 'ry fear He march - es proudly to the fray Be-
hues in splen-dor bright-ly glow; En-shrin'd in beau-ty and in love He
own tri - um-phant flag un-furl'd Must fight till Truth, her vic-t'ries won, In

cour - age scorn-ing ev - 'ry fear He march - es proud-ly to the fray Be-
hues in splen-dor bright-ly glow; En-shrin'd in beau-ty and in love He
own tri - um-phant flag un-furl'd Must fight till Truth, her vic-t'ries won, In

neath the flag he holds so dear. . .
keeps it safe from ev - 'ry foe. . .
love and peace shall rule the world. . .

neath the flag he holds so dear. . .
keeps it safe from ev - 'ry foe. . .
love and peace shall rule the world. . .

f *Repeat twice (from meas. 5.)*

Annie Laurie

Unison Song for Basses, with Three-Part Humming Accompaniment

Douglas of Fingland

Lady John Scott
Arr. by C. B. Rich

1. Max-wel-ton's braes are bon-nie, Where ear-ly fa's the dew; And 'twas there that An-nie Lau-rie Gave me her prom-ise true, Gave me her prom-ise true, Which ne'er for-got will be, And for

2. Her brow is like the snaw-drift, Her throat is like the swan; Her face it is the fair-est, That e'er the sun shone on; That e'er the sun shone on; And dark blue is her e'e, And for

Copyright, 1909, by Silver, Burdett and Company

Annie Laurie

Lau - rie 16

bon - nie An - nie Lau - rie .... I'd dee!

bon - nie An - nie Lau - rie ..... I'd dee, I'd dee!

bon - nie An - nie Lau - rie, I'd lay me down and dee!

My Heart's in the Highlands
Three-Part Song for Equal Voices

ROBERT BURNS

Scotch Folksong

Andante

1. My heart's in the high-lands, my heart is not here; My heart's in the high-lands a-chas-ing the deer; A-chas-ing the wild deer and fol-l'wing the roe, My heart's in the high-lands, wher-ev-er I go.
2. Fare-well to the high-lands, fare-well to the North, The birth-place of val - or, the coun-try of worth; Wher-ev-er I wan-der, wher-ev-er I rove, The hills of the high-lands for-ev-er I love.
3. Fare-well to the moun-tains, high=cov-er'd with snow; Fare - well to the straths and green val-leys be-low; Fare-well to the for-ests and wild=hang-ing woods; Fare-well to the tor-rents and loud=pour-ing floods.

Song Should Breathe

Three-part or Four-part Song (Optional Bass)

Barry Cornwall   L. Van Beethoven

Tyrolienne

With Humming Accompaniment and Four-Part Refrain

David K. Stevens

Carrie Bullard

1. In the ear-ly dawn, When the waking morn Tips the mountain peak with ro-sy
2. When the set-ting sun Tells the day is done Homeward now the sheep and shepherd

glow, With a heart of joy Sings the shepherd boy: "Oo - la, la - ee, la - ee, la - ee,
go; And the hour is glad For the wea-ry lad Sing-ing "Oo-la, la-ee, la-ee,

Copyright, 1909, by Silver, Burdett & Company

Over the Moonlit Sea

Barcarolle, in Three or Four Parts (Optional Bass)

DAVID K. STEVENS   From " Pinafore," ARTHUR SULLIVAN

1. O - ver the moon-lit sea   Comes the sil - ver-y sound of tune-ful glee; A
2. Calm - ly the Queen of Night   Touch-es all with a beam of gold-en light; A
3. Faint - er the dy-ing strain— Soft-ly fad - ing the sound of sweet re-frain, Their

bar - ca-rolle they sing—   Hark! how their mer - ry voic - es ring!
thous - and jew-els play,   Bright—spark-ling on the fly - ing spray;
bar - ca-rolle is o'er,   See! they have touched the dis - tant shore.

Copyright, 1909, by SILVER, BURDETT & COMPANY

Christmas Bells

HENRY WADSWORTH LONGFELLOW

CHARLES FONTEYN MANNEY

Copyright, 1909, by SILVER, BURDETT & COMPANY

Christmas Bells

Robin Adair

Unison Song for Basses, with Three-Part Humming Accompaniment

Lady Keppel (?)

Scotch Folksong
Arr. by C. B. Rich

1. What's this dull town to me? Rob-in's not near.
2. What made th'as-sem-bly shine? Rob-in A-dair!
3. But now thou'rt far from me, Rob-in A-dair!

What was't I wish'd to see, What wish'd to hear? Where's all the joy and mirth
What made the ball so fine? Ro-bin was there. What, when the play was o'er,
And now thou'rt cold to me, Ro-bin A-dair; Yet he I lov'd so well

Rob-in A-dair!
Rob-in A-dair!
Rob-in A-dair!

That made this town a heav'n on earth? O, they're all fled with thee, Rob-in A-dair!
What made my heart so sore? O, it was part-ing with Rob-in A-dair!
Still in my heart shall dwell. O, I can ne'er for-get Rob-in A-dair!

Copyright, 1909, by Silver, Burdett and Company

Ring on, Ye Bells

Three-Part or Four-Part Song (Optional Bass)

FRANZ ABT

Moderato ma non troppo

1. Ring on, ye bells! your sil - ver chimes Sound sweet-ly in the sum-mer air; They
2. Your mu - sic is a sooth-ing balm, A sol - ace to a wea-ry breast. Up -
3. Like life your tones are grave and gay, In sor - row you can draw a tear; Then

ech - o thoughts of oth - er times, Of oth - er homes in oth - er climes, And fa - ces
on an e - ven cool and calm, Who has not felt that po - tent charm That brings the
comes a peal of joy, to say That grief and woe must flee a - way, But smiles may

young and fair, And fa - ces young and fair! Ring on, ye bells, ring on! ring on! Ring
wea - ry rest, That brings the wea-ry rest? Ring on, ye bells, ring on! ring on! Ring
lin - ger near, But smiles may lin-ger near! Ring on, ye bells, ring on! ring on! Ring

on, ye bells, ring on, ring on! Ring on, ye bells, ring on! Ring on, ring on, ring on!

on, ye bells, ring on, ring on! Ring on, ye bells, ring on, ring on! Ring on, ring on, ring on!

The Merry Lark
For Four-Part Chorus

JOHN BENNETT

GEORGE B. NÉVIN

1. Hey, lad-die, hark to the mer-ry, mer-ry lark, How high he sing-eth clear.
2. God bless us all, my jol-ly gen-tle-men, We'll mer-ry be to-day;

1. Hey, lad-die, hark to the mer-ry, mer-ry lark, How high he sing-eth clear.
2. God bless us all, my jol-ly gen-tle-men, We'll mer-ry be to-day;

Oh, a morn in spring is the sweet-est thing That com-eth in all the year.
For the sky-lark sings till the green-wood rings, And it is the month of May.

Oh, a morn in spring is the sweet-est thing That com-eth in all the year.
For the sky-lark sings till the green-wood rings, And it is the month of May.

March of the Victors

Unison Song, with Four-Part Chorus

Nixon Waterman

From "Aida"
Giuseppe Verdi

f Allegro maestoso

1. Hail, all hail! the vic - tors are re - turn - ing; Wave, flags, wave! o'er sol - diers brave and
2. Cheer, all cheer! the flags so proud - ly wav - ing, Greet with joy the ban - ner in the

true: See they come! their hearts with val - or burn - ing, 'Neath their flag, the proud red, white and
sky; Crown with song the ones who, dan - ger brav - ing, Still go forth to con - quer or to

blue. On they pressed, the old flag o - ver them; Clashed their sa - bres, blow on blow;
die. Armed with right and pur - pose glo - ri - ous, Marched they forth to meet the foe;

Earth was wait - ing there to cov - er them Had they fall'n be - fore the foe.
Now up - on their deeds vic - to - ri - ous Let us fond - est praise be - stow.

Copyright, 1909, by Silver, Burdett & Company

Chorus

20

Shot and shell a-round them thickly fly - ing, Fierce and long the dark and aw - ful fray;
Hail, all hail! the vic - tors are re - turn-ing; Wave, flags, wave! o'er sol-diers brave and true;

Shot and shell a - round them thick-ly fly - ing, Fierce and long the dark and aw - ful fray;
Hail, all hail! the vic - tors are re - turn - ing; Wave, flags, wave! o'er sol-diers brave and true;

Shrank they not a-mid the dead and dy - ing, Theirs to go where glo - ry led the way.
See, they come! their hearts with val-or burn - ing, 'Neath their flag, the proud red, white and blue.

Shrank they not a - mid the dead and dy - ing, Theirs to go where glo - ry led the way.
See, they come! their hearts with val - or burn - ing, 'Neath their flag, the proud red, white and blue.

The Jolly Tar

Unison Song for Basses, with Four-Part Chorus

Nixon Waterman

Max Mohr

Bass Solo, or Unison Chorus

1. When waves have rocked themselves a-sleep,
3. And here is a word for you, my lad,

Moderato risoluto

Where the wild sea = chil-dren play, And a spell is laid up-on the deep To
Wher-ev-er you chance to be, Or..if you're gay or if you're sad, Or

keep the winds a-way; Then try-ing to stir the i-dle crew And help the ship a-
on the land or sea; When skies are dark and fogs pre-vail, And ev-'ry-thing is

long, As we lie a-drift in the boundless blue, I sing this rous-ing song:
wrong, Oh, that's the time to fill your sail With just this rous-ing (To Meas. 54)

Copyright, 1909, by SILVER, BURDETT AND COMPANY

shocks;   Then try - ing to think of a way   to make the hearts of the sail - ors

strong, And   smooth the   sea   for the old ship's sake, I   sing this jo - vial   song:

The winds   may sleep, the winds   may blow; Yo - ho! Yo - ho! Yo -

The winds   may sleep, the winds   may blow; Yo - ho! Yo - ho! Yo -

The winds   may sleep, the winds   may blow; Yo - ho! Yo - ho! Yo -

song.   The winds   may sleep, the winds   may blow; Yo - ho! Yo - ho! Yo -

From the Starry Heavens High

ELIZABETH E. FOULKE

French Christmas Song

1. From the star - ry heav-ens high, Strains of joy ex - ult - ant ring; And the hills of
2. Shepherds, mute with ho - ly joy, List the mes - sage from a - bove; Peace on earth with -
3. Haste, O haste, the tid-ings bear, Far and wide o'er all the earth; Till the na - tions

earth re - ply, All their mu - sic ech - o - ing. Glo - - - - - -
out al - loy, Now be - gins the reign of love. Glo - - - - - -
ev - 'ry-where, Sing the ho - ly Sav-iour's birth. Glo - - - - - -

- - - - - - ri - a in ex - cel - sis De - o, De - - o.

Slumber Song

Unison Song for All Voices

NIXON WATERMAN   GEORGE HENRY HOWARD

soft, re - sign - ing In a dream we drift a - way, Then to slum - ber ..
fond - ly cling - ing, In - to Slum - ber - land we go, In our dreams still ..
dreams is set - ting Toward a har - bor calm and fair, In a ship of ...

soft re - sign - ing, we drift a - way. Peace - ful - ly drift - ing,
fond - ly cling - ing, To slum - ber we go. Peace - ful - ly drift - ing,
dreams is set - ting, To slum - ber fair. Peace - ful - ly drift - ing,

Far, far a - way far a - way, far a - way, Far, far a - way.

The Waterfall

Nixon Waterman

W. W. Gilchrist

Copyright, 1909, by Silver, Burdett & Company

Seek-ing its wind - ing way.
Won-der-ful mys - ter - y !

Won - der-ful mys - ter - y.
Seek - ing its wind - ing way.

Ma - ny a farm it glides lei - sure-ly past,
Twist-ing and turn-ing it comes from its source,

Ma - ny a farm it glides lei - sure-ly past,
Twist-ing and turn - ing, it comes from its source,

For-est and mead-ow-land fair, ... Chant-ing a song till it reach-es, at last, The
Wind-ing and curv-ing a - gain, ... Dream-i - ly on, till it finds in its course The

For-est and mead-ow-land fair,
Wind-ing and curv-ing a - gain,

Chant-ing a song till it reach-es, at last, The
Dream-i - ly on, till it finds in its course The

The Waterfall

Lincoln

Nixon Waterman

L. B. Marshall

1. The child .. of low - ly ones of earth, With - in that hum - ble cab - in born; ... The splen - did day that
2. Your deeds .. with ho - ly pur - pose fraught, Your toil with hon - ors rich - ly crown'd, .. To all .. the sons of
3. A - bove .. a na - tion's stress and strife, Your cher - ished name, a bea - con bright, ... Shall guide .. us through the

Lincoln

gave you birth Shall all our gold-en years a-dorn. From out your crude, un-
earth have brought A zeal more no - ble, more profound. Your home - ly smiles, your
ways of life, To gra - cious goals of truth and right. And from that hum - ble

gave you birth Shall all our gold-en years a-dorn. From out your crude, un -
earth have brought A zeal more no - ble, more profound. Your home - ly smiles, your
ways of life, To gra - cious goals of truth and right. And from that hum - ble

let - ter'd youth You came, and with a light di-vine, A -
home - ly tears, Your joys and sor - rows strange - ly blent, Shall
cab - in door, The path you trod, a care - less boy, Shall

let - ter'd youth You came, and with a light di - vine, A -
home - ly tears, Your joys and sor - rows strange-ly blent, Shall
cab - in door, The path you trod, a care - less boy, Shall

Old Black Joe

Unison Song for Basses, with Two-Part Vocal Accompaniment

STEPHEN C. FOSTER

STEPHEN C. FOSTER
Arr. by C. B. RICH

1. Gone are the days when my heart was young and gay,
2. Why do I weep when my heart should feel no pain?
3. Where are the hearts once so hap-py and so free? The

Gone are my friends, Mm . .
Why do I sigh? Mm . .
Chil - dren so dear, Mm . .

Gone are my friends from the cot - ton - fields a - way, Gone from the
Why do I sigh that my friends come not a - gain? Griev - ing for
chil - dren so dear that I held up - on my knee? Gone to the

I hear their gen - tle voic - es call - ing

earth to a bet - ter land, I know, I hear their gen - tle voic - es call - ing
forms now de - part - ed long a - go? I hear their gen - tle voic - es call - ing
shore where my soul has long'd to go! I hear their gen - tle voic - es call - ing

Copyright, 1909, by SILVER, BURDETT & COMPANY

Old Black Joe

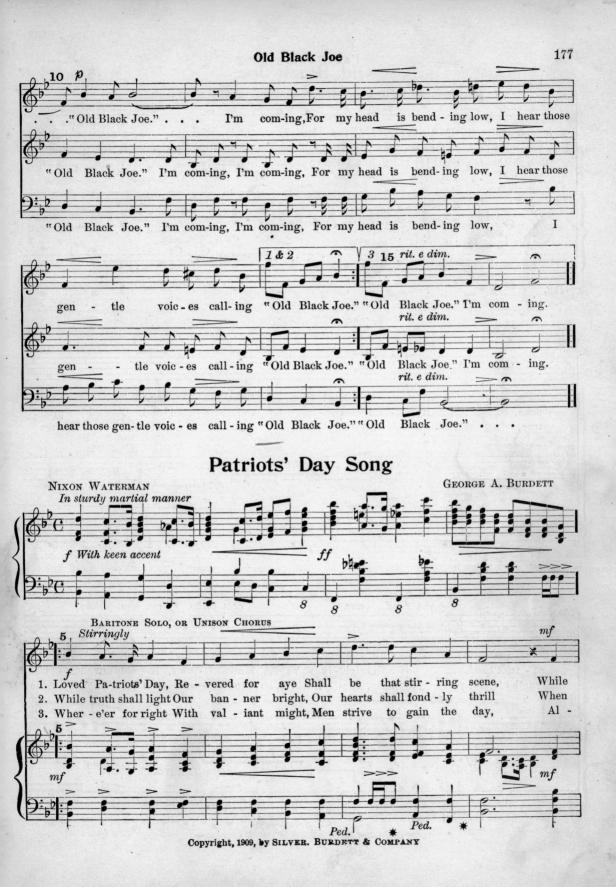

... "Old Black Joe." ... I'm com-ing, For my head is bend-ing low, I hear those

"Old Black Joe." I'm com-ing, I'm com-ing, For my head is bend-ing low, I hear those

"Old Black Joe." I'm com-ing, I'm com-ing, For my head is bend-ing low, I

gen - tle voic-es call-ing "Old Black Joe." "Old Black Joe." I'm com - ing.

gen - tle voic-es call-ing "Old Black Joe." "Old Black Joe." I'm com - ing.

hear those gen- tle voic- es call - ing "Old Black Joe." "Old Black Joe." ...

Patriots' Day Song

Nixon Waterman

George A. Burdett

In sturdy martial manner

f With keen accent

Baritone Solo, or Unison Chorus

Stirringly

1. Loved Pa-triots' Day, Re - vered for aye Shall be that stir - ring scene, While
2. While truth shall light Our ban - ner bright, Our hearts shall fond - ly thrill When
3. Wher - e'er for right With val - iant might, Men strive to gain the day, Al -

Copyright, 1909, by Silver, Burdett & Company

See, the Conquering Hero Comes

Dr. MORELL
Marziale e maestoso

From "Judas Maccabæus," G. F. HÄNDEL

The Stage=Coach

NIXON WATERMAN

CHARLES FONTEYN MANNEY

Moderately fast, with good accent

SOLO, OR UNISON

1. Be - fore the tire - less steed of steam Has trod his i - ron track, Be -
2. The trail it leaves o'er prai - ries wide Or hills that greet the sky, Is
3. Where once the In - dian's blaz - ing fire Made bright the for - est shade Shall

fore the head-light's search-ing gleam Has waved the shad-ows back; Where yet the wild beast
fol - low'd by a swell - ing tide Of men with pur - pose high; Where wheel has nev - er
rise the town with glit-t'ring spire And bus - y mart of trade; And then the tire - less

builds its den And na - ture holds her sway, Thro' haunts of rough and rug - ged men The
roll'd be - fore, In re - gions strange and new, The stage=coach comes and ev - er - more Still
steed of steam Shall cause to dis - ap - pear The stage=coach with its four-horse team That

Gayly the Troubadour

Unison Song for Basses, with Vocal Accompaniment

T. H. BAYLY

T. H. BAYLY
Arr. by C. B. RICH

Thrum, thrum, thrum, thrum, thrum, etc.

Thrum, thrum, thrum, thrum, thrum, etc.

1. Gay - ly   the
2. She   for   the
3. Hark ! 'twas the

Trou - ba - dour touched   his gui - tar, . . When   he   was hast - en - ing
Trou - ba - dour hope - less - ly wept, . Sad - ly she tho't of   him
Trou - ba - dour breath - ing her name, . . Un - der the bat - tle - ment

Copyright, 1909, by SILVER, BURDETT & COMPANY

thrum, thrum. Sing - ing, thrum, thrum, etc. . . . .

thrum, thrum. Sing - ing, thrum, thrum, etc. . . . .

home from the war.   "From Pal - es - tine hith - er   I   come;
when oth - ers slept.   "In search of   thee would   I might roam!
soft - ly he came.   "From Pal - es - tine hith - er   I   come;

La - dye Love,   La - dye Love, wel - come   me home!"
Trou - ba - dour, Trou - ba - dour, come   to   thy home."
La - dye Love,   La - dye Love, wel - come   me (Omit . . . .)

home." . . . .

Washington

With Solos or Unisons and Four-Part Chorus

Nixon Waterman

L. B. Marshall

1. Lov'd Washington! In mem-'ry dear We hold thy cher-ish'd name That
2. When Freedom's no-ble cause was born, To glo-ri-fy our land, On
3. Em-blaz-on'd on our gold-en sky A thousand names shall shine, Yet

gleams a-mid the splen-dor, clear, Of Truth's un-dy-ing flame. With glow-ing faith thy
that tem-pest-uous na-tal morn, 'Twas guard-ed by thy hand. When first her sons with
none, how-ev-er bright and high, Can o-ver-shad-ow thine. And while up-on the

deeds en-dow Our fond-est hopes, to-day, . . An ev-er-shin-ing bea-con, thou, To
val-or bright Wreath'd fair Co-lum-bia's brow, . . Thy zeal shone forth to lead the right As
breeze shall swell Our ban-ner proud and free, . . In grateful praise our tho'ts shall dwell, Lov'd

The Postilion's Song

For Four-Part Chorus

David K. Stevens

Henry Hadley

Very fast and light

(Postilion's Horn)

1. The earl and his la - dy are trav' - ling late, So
2. The earl and his la - dy are trav' - ling far, And
3. The earl and his la - dy are trav' - ling fast, Nor

1. The earl and his la - dy are trav' - ling late, So
2. The earl and his la - dy are trav' - ling far, And
3. The earl and his la - dy are trav' - ling fast, Nor

on   to   the next   re - lay;   We're stop-ping for naught but the toll = man's gate   For the
noth - ing   our course shall stay;   No Jack o' the Heath our ad - vance shall bar   For the
ev - er   will brook de - lay;   The cas - tle we'll win if the pace can last,   For the

on   to   the next   re - lay;   We're stop-ping for naught but the toll = man's gate   For the
noth - ing   our course shall stay;   No Jack o' the Heath our ad - vance shall bar   For the
ev - er   will brook de - lay;   The cas - tle we'll win if the pace can last,   For the

Copyright, 1909, by SILVER, BURDETT & COMPANY

earl and his la - dy are trav' - ling late, With a crack of the whip and a -
earl and his la - dy are trav' - ling late, With a crack of the whip and a -

way! A - way! With a crack of the whip—a - way! Stead - y, my lads,
way! A - way! With a crack of the whip—a - way! Stead - y, my lads,

Stead - y, my lads, so - ho!.. so - ho!.. The rain may beat and the
Stead - y, my lads, so - ho! . . . so - ho! The rain may beat and the

wind may blow, But clat - ter - tat - tat! is the way we go,   A -

A - way!

A - way! . . . .

A-way!

way!   A - way   we   go.   Snap! Crack! A - way!   But clat - ter - tat - tat is the

way . . . .   we   go. . . .

But clat - ter - tat - tat is the   way   we   go, . .   we   go. . . .

America

S. F. SMITH

HENRY CAREY

1. My coun-try! 'tis of thee,Sweet land of lib-er-ty, Of thee I sing; Land where my
2. My na-tive coun-try,thee,Land of the no-ble,free,Thy name I love; I love thy
3. Let mu-sic swell the breeze,And ring from all the trees Sweet freedom's song. Let mor-tal
4. Our fa-thers' God! to Thee, Au-thor of lib-er-ty, To Thee we sing! Long may our

fa-thers died! Land of the Pilgrim's pride! From ev-'ry moun-tain side Let free-dom ring!
rocks and rills,Thy woods and templed hills; My heart with rap-ture thrills Like that a-bove.
tongues a-wake,Let all that breathe par-take, Let rocks their si-lence break,—The sound pro-long.
land be bright With freedom's ho-ly light; Pro-tect us by Thy might, Great God,our King.

Hymn of Peace*

J. ANNIE BENSE

L. B. MARSHALL

1. Great Land,in a-ges old By seer and proph-et told, Land of the free; Throw wide thy
2. Up-on thy throb-bing breast May ev-'ry soul find rest, Like hom-ing dove! May all the
3. O land of tow-'ring hills, Broad streams and myr-iad rills And sa-cred sod, Dear land,from

por-tals broad To o-cean's might-y horde,Who,stirred with one ac-cord, Now fly to thee!
winds that thrill From all the snow-capped hill Speak forth thy glorious will, In words of love!
shore to shore, Where o-cean's bil-lows roar,May peace brood ev-er-more,The Peace,the Peace of God!

* This hymn may be sung to the tune of "America."

The Star=Spangled Banner

FRANCIS SCOTT KEY

SAMUEL ARNOLD

SOLO, OR VOICES IN UNISON

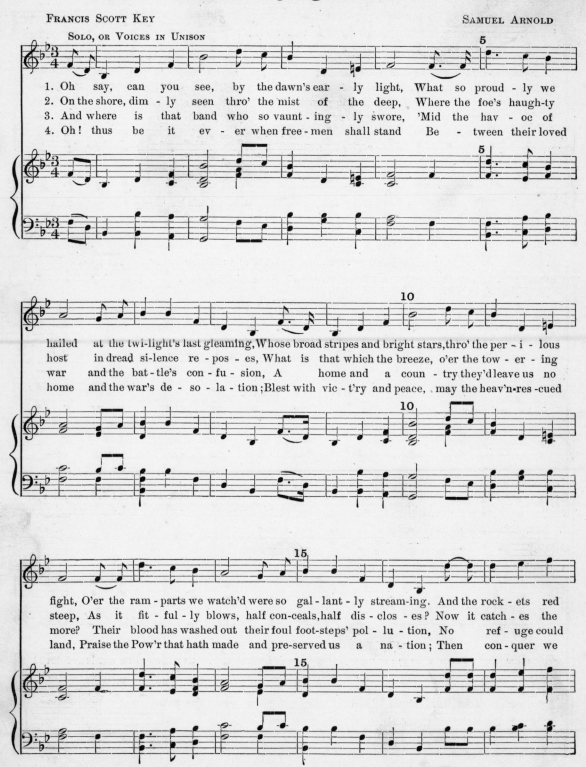

1. Oh say, can you see, by the dawn's ear - ly light, What so proud - ly we
2. On the shore, dim - ly seen thro' the mist of the deep, Where the foe's haugh - ty
3. And where is that band who so vaunt - ing - ly swore, 'Mid the hav - oc of
4. Oh! thus be it ev - er when free - men shall stand Be - tween their loved

hailed at the twi - light's last gleaming, Whose broad stripes and bright stars, thro' the per - i - lous
host in dread si - lence re - pos - es, What is that which the breeze, o'er the tow - er - ing
war and the bat - tle's con - fu - sion, A home and a coun - try they'd leave us no
home and the war's de - so - la - tion; Blest with vic - t'ry and peace, may the heav'n res - cued

fight, O'er the ram - parts we watch'd were so gal - lant - ly stream - ing. And the rock - ets red
steep, As it fit - ful - ly blows, half con - ceals, half dis - clos - es? Now it catch - es the
more? Their blood has washed out their foul foot-steps' pol - lu - tion, No ref - uge could
land, Praise the Pow'r that hath made and pre - served us a na - tion; Then con - quer we

glare, the bombs bursting in air, Gave proof thro' the night that our flag was still there.
gleam of the morn-ing's first beam, In full glo - ry re - flect - ed, now shines on the stream.
save the hire - ling and slave, From the ter - ror of flight, or the gloom of the grave.
must, when our cause it is just, And this be our mot - to: "In God is our trust."

CHORUS ff

1. Oh! . say, does that star = span - gled ban - ner yet
2. 'Tis the star = span - gled ban - ner, oh! long may it
3. And the star = span - gled ban - ner in tri - umph doth
4. And the star = span - gled ban - ner in tri - umph shall

1. Oh! say, does that star - span - gled ban - ner yet
2. 'Tis the star - span - gled ban - ner, oh! long may it
3. And the star = span - gled ban - ner in tri - umph doth
4. And the star = span - gled ban - ner in tri - umph shall

(*Accompanist plays voice-parts*)

wave, O'er the land of the free and the home of the brave.

wave, O'er the land of the free and the home of the brave.

Columbia, the Gem of the Ocean

D. T. Shaw

SOLO, OR VOICES IN UNISON

1. O Co-lum - bia! the gem of the o-cean, The home of the brave and the free, The
2. When war wing'd its wide des - o - la-tion, And threaten'd the land to de - form, The
3. The star-span-gled ban-ner bring hither, O'er Co-lum-bia's sons let it wave; May the

Maestoso

shrine of each patriot's de - vo-tion, A world of-fers hom-age to thee; Thy
ark, then, of freedom's foundation, Co lum bia, rode safe thro' the storm; With her
wreaths they have won never with-er, Nor its stars cease to shine on the brave; May the

mandates make he - roes as-sem-ble, When Lib - er - ty's form stands in view;
gar-lands of vic - t'ry around her, When so proud - ly she bore her brave crew,
ser - vice u - nit - ed ne'er sev - er, But hold to their col - ors so true;

cres. . . . . f **15**

Thy ban-ners make tyr-an - ny trem-ble, When borne by the red, white and blue !
With her flag proud-ly floating be-fore her, The boast of the red, white and blue !
The ar-my and na-vy for - ev - er, Three cheers for the red, white and blue !

S. 1 Chorus
ff   *mp* *cres. . . . .* **20** *ff*

S. 2
When borne by the red, white and blue, When borne by the red, white and blue, Thy
The boast of the red, white and blue, The boast of the red, white and blue, With her
Three cheers for the red, white and blue, Three cheers for the red, white and blue, The

T.
ff   *mp*   *ff*

A.
When borne by the red, white and blue, When borne by the red, white and blue, Thy
The boast of the red, white and blue, The boast of the red, white and blue, With her
Three cheers for the red, white and blue, Three cheers for the red, white and blue, The

B.
ff   *mp* *cres. . . . .* *ff*

(Accompanist plays voice-parts or repeats accompaniment of measures 9-16.)

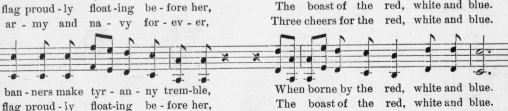

ban -ners make tyr - an - ny trem-ble, When borne by the red, white and blue.
flag proud - ly float-ing be - fore her, The boast of the red, white and blue.
ar - my and na - vy for - ev - er, Three cheers for the red, white and blue.

ban -ners make tyr - an - ny trem-ble, When borne by the red, white and blue.
flag proud - ly float-ing be - fore her, The boast of the red, white and blue.
ar - my and na - vy for - ev - er, Three cheers for the red, white and blue.

The Nation's Heroes

David K. Stevens

L. B. Marshall

1. Be-neath a spread-ing robe of ver - dure, Where bloom the fairest flow'rs of May, In
2. For all that fell in oth - er strug-gles, On west - ern plain and al - ien land, Of
3. And what of them that sailed the o - cean, Whose arms were stout, whose hearts were brave? Of

1. Be-neath a spread-ing robe of ver - dure, Where bloom the fairest flow'rs of May, In
2. For all that fell in oth - er strug-gles, On west - ern plain and al - ien land, Of
3. And what of them that sailed the o - cean, Whose arms were stout, whose hearts were brave? Of

Where bloom the fair - est flow'rs of May, In
On west - ern plain and al - ien land, We
Whose arms were stout, whose hearts were brave, Of

peace e - ter - nal now are sleep-ing The men who wore the Blue and Gray. O'er
mem - o - ry we lay the to - ken Up - on their beds with ten - der hand. What
them that fell on ships of bat - tle And found their rest be - neath the wave? No

peace e - ter - nal now are sleep-ing The men who wore the Blue and Gray. O'er
mem - o - ry we lay the to - ken Up - on their beds with ten - der hand. What
them that fell on ships of bat - tle And found their rest be - neath the wave? No

peace now are sleep - ing
lay now the to - ken
them in ships of bat - tle

countless mounds where lie our he - roes The ban-ners of our coun-try wave; The
thought had ye, de - vot - ed war-riors, Of Glo - ry or her sis - ter, Fame? The
green-clad mounds for ye, our sea - men, For lov-ing hands to guard and tend; Our

countless mounds where lie our he - roes The ban-ners of our coun-try wave; (The ban-ners wave,) The
thought had ye, de - vot - ed war-riors, Of Glo - ry or her sis - ter, Fame? (What tho't of Fame?) The
green-clad mounds for ye, our sea - men, For lov - ing hands to guard and tend; (To guard and tend;) Our

Copyright, 1909, by Silver, Burdett & Company

Dixie

Solo or Unison Chorus, with Four-Part Refrain

DAN EMMETT

Allegro mf

1. I wish I was in de land ob cot-ton, Old times dar am not for-got-ten,
2. Dar's buck-wheat cakes an' In-gen bat-ter, Makes you fat or a lit-tle fat-ter;

Look a - way! Look a - way! Look a - way! Dix-ie Land. In Dix-ie Land whar
Look a - way! Look a - way! Look a - way! Dix-ie Land. Den hoe it down an'

I was born in, Ear-ly on one frost-y morn-in', Look a - way! Look a-
scratch your grab-ble, To Dix-ie's land I'm bound to trab-ble, Look a - way! Look a-

The Watch by the Rhine

MAX SCHNECKENBURGER

KARL WILHELM

S. 1 *Allegro marziale*

S. 2

1. A cry is heard like thun - der sound, The clash of swords, the waves rebound; "The
2. A myr - iad voic - es join the cry, A myr - iad glan - ces flash re - ply, Each
3. The oath re-sounds, the stream runs by, The ban - ners flut - ter out on high, The

T.

A.

1. A cry is heard like thun - der sound, The clash of swords, the waves rebound; "The
2. A myr - iad voic - es join the cry, A myr - iad glan - ces flash re - ply, Each
3. The oath re-sounds, the stream runs by, The ban - ners flut - ter out on high, The

B.

Rhine, the Rhine, our riv - er free, Who will its brave de - fend - ers be?"
pa - triot, hon - est, true and bold, The sa - cred boun - da - ry will hold!
Rhine, the Rhine, our riv - er free, We all will its de - fend - ers be!

Rhine, the Rhine, our riv - er free, Who will its brave de - fend - ers be?"
pa - triot, hon - est, true and bold, The sa - cred boun - da - ry will hold!
Rhine, the Rhine, our riv - er free, We all will its de - fend - ers be!

CHORUS 10

Dear Fa - ther-land, may peace be thine! Dear Fa - ther-land, may peace be thine, Fast stands and

Dear Fa - ther-land, may peace be thine! Dear Fa - ther-land, may peace be thine, Fast stands and

National Hymn

D. C. ROBERTS
Marziale

G. W. WARREN

[*Small notes for Piano or Organ*]

1. God of our fa - thers, whose al - might - y hand
2. Thy love di - vine hath led us in the past;
3. From war's a - larms, from dead - ly pes - ti - lence,
4. Re - fresh Thy peo - ple on their toil - some way,

Leads forth in beau - ty all the star - ry band Of shin - ing worlds in
In this free land by Thee our lot is cast; Be Thou our rul - er,
Be Thy strong arm our ev - er sure de - fence; Thy true re - lig - ion
Lead us from night to nev - er - end - ing day; Fill all our lives with

splendor thro' the skies, Our grate - ful songs be - fore Thy throne a - rise.
guardian, guide and stay, Thy word our law, Thy paths our chos - en way.
in our hearts in - crease, Thy boun - teous good - ness nour - ish us in peace.
love and grace di - vine, And glo - ry, laud and praise be ev - er Thine. A - MEN.

By permission of THE CENTURY COMPANY

Decoration Day

Margaret E. Sangster

F. Kücken

Andante con espressione

1. Year by year the sun and rain, O - ver val - ley, o - ver
2. Year by year with mar - tial drum, Young and glad, the sol - diers
3. Ah, the world is bright and gay On their Dec - o - ra - tion

plain, Beams or falls where low they lie, Who once wrought be -
come; Ban - nered pomp of spring - time waves O'er the war - riors'
Day; Flowers are fling - ing per - fume rare, Wings are glanc - ing

neath the sky. Gal - lant, loy - al, brave and strong, Well they
qui - et graves; Chil - dren sing with voi - ces sweet, Hast - ing
through the air, Ros - es wave a cov - er - let, Lil - ies

Sheet music with lyrics:

Verse lines (top staff):
fought to right the wrong. Here they slum - ber; ... no
on ... with trip - ping feet. Vet - 'rans march in .... thin -
bid .. us not for - get, And the stars their ... vig -

(middle staff lyrics):
Here they slum - ber; no
Vet - 'rans march in thin -
And the stars their vig -

(second system lyrics):
a - larms Wake these wea - ry men = at = arms. ....
ning line, Tell - ing tales of auld lang syne. ....
ils keep, Night - ly, while the he - roes sleep. .....

(repeated lower staff):
a - larms Wake these wea - ry men = at = arms. ....
ning line, Tell - ing tales of auld lang syne. ....
ils keep, Night - ly, while the he - roes sleep. .....

Russian Hymn

S. F. SMITH

ALEXIS LVOFF

Maestoso

1. God ev - er glo - ri - ous ! Sov-'reign of na - tions, Wav - ing the ban - ner of Peace o'er our land ;
2. Still may Thy blessing rest, Fa -ther most ho - ly, O - ver each mountain, rock, riv - er, and shore ;

Thine is the vic - to - ry, Thine the sal - va - tion, Strong to de - liv - er Own we Thy hand.
Sing al - le - lu - ia ! Shout in ho - san - nas ! God keep our coun - try Free ev - er-more!

Memorial Day

SAMUEL FRANCIS SMITH

L. B. MARSHALL

1. Not cost - ly domes, nor mar - ble tow'rs Shall mark where friend - ship comes to
2. They rest in ma - ny a shad - ed vale, By and be - neath the sound - ing
3. They mer - it all our hearts can give, Our prais - es and our love they
4. Blest be the land for which they fought, The land where Free - dom's ban - ners

weep; Let clust'ring vines and fra - grant flow'rs, Tell where the na - tion's he - roes sleep.
sea; The for - est winds their re - quiem wail, The glo - rious sons of lib - er - ty.
claim; Long shall their pre - cious names sur - vive, Held sa - cred by im - mor - tal fame.
wave. The land by blood and treas - ure bought, Where dwell the free, where sleep the brave.

American Hymn

Come, Thou Almighty King

C. WESLEY

F. GIARDINI

1. Come, Thou Al-might-y King! Help us Thy name to sing; Help us to praise! Fa-ther all-
2. Come, Thou all-gra-cious Lord, By heav'n and earth a-dored, Our pray'r at-tend! Come, and Thy
3. Nev-er from us de-part; Rule Thou in ev-'ry heart, Hence, ev-er-more. Thy sov-'reign

glo-ri-ous, O'er all vic-to-ri-ous, Come and reign o-ver us, An-cient of days!
chil-dren bless; Give Thy good word suc-cess; Make Thine own ho-li-ness On us de-scend.
ma-jes-ty May we in glo-ry see, And to e-ter-ni-ty Love and a-dore.

Lead, Kindly Light

J. H. NEWMAN

J. B. DYKES

1. Lead, kind-ly Light, a-mid th' en-cir-cling gloom, Lead Thou me on! The night is
2. I was not ev-er thus, nor pray'd that Thou Shouldst lead me on. I lov'd to
3. So long Thy pow'r has blest me, sure it still Will lead me on O'er moor and

dark, and I am far from home, Lead Thou me on! Keep Thou my feet, I
choose and see my path, but now Lead Thou me on! I lov'd the gar-ish
fen, o'er crag and tor-rent, till The night is gone. And with the morn those

do not ask to see . . The dis-tant scene; one step e-nough for me.
day, and spite of fears. Pride ruled my will: re-mem-ber not past years!
an-gel fa-ces smile, . Which I have lov'd long since and lost a-while.

The King of Love

W. H. Baker

J. B. Dykes

1. The King of love my Shep-herd is, Whose good - ness fail - eth nev - er;
2. Where streams of liv - ing wa - ter flow, My ran - somed soul He lead - eth,
3. Per - verse and fool - ish, oft I strayed, But yet in love He sought me,
4. And so through all the length of days Thy good - ness fail - eth nev - er;

I noth - ing lack if I am His, And He is mine for - ev - er.
And, where the ver - dant pas - tures grow, With food ce - les - tial feed - eth.
And on His shoul - der gen - tly laid, And home, re - joic - ing, brought me.
Good Shep - herd, may I sing Thy praise With - in Thy house for - ev - er.

Lord God of Morning

J. Keble

L. Van Beethoven

1. Lord God of morn - ing and .. of night, We thank Thee for Thy gifts . of light;
2. Fresh hopes have wak - ened in ... the heart, Fresh force to do our dai - ly part;
3. Praise God, our Mak - er and .. our Friend; Praise Him thro' time, till time shall end;

As in the dawn the shad - ows fly, We seem to find Thee now more nigh.
Thy slum - ber = gifts our strength re-store, Through-out the day to serve Thee more.
Till psalm and song His name a - dore, Thro' Heaven's great day of Ev - er - more.

When Morning Gilds the Skies

E. CASWALL

J. BARNBY

Allegro moderato

1. When morn-ing gilds the skies, My heart a - wak-ing cries, Thy name, O God, be praised;
2. Does sad - ness fill my mind? A sol - ace here I find, Thy name, O God, be praised;
3. The night be-comes as day, When from the heart we say, Thy name, O God, be praised;
4. In heav'n's e - ter - nal bliss The love-liest strain is this, Thy name, O God, be praised;

A - like at work or pray'r, On Thee I cast my care, Thy name, O God, be praised.
Or fades my earthly bliss, My com-fort still is this, Thy name, O God, be praised.
The pow'rs of darkness fear When this sweet chant they hear, Thy name, O God, be praised.
Let air, and sea, and sky, From depth to height re - ply, Thy name, O God, be praised.

The Lord is King

J. COUDER

L. VAN BEETHOVEN

1. The Lord is King! lift up thy voice, O earth; and all ye heav'ns re - joice;
2. The Lord is King! who then shall dare Re - sist His will, dis-trust His care,
3. One Lord, one em - pire all se - cures, He reigns, and life and death are yours.

From world to world, the joy shall ring, The Lord om - nip - o - tent is King.
Or mur - mur at . . . His wise de - crees, Or doubt His roy - al prom - is - es?
Through earth and heaven one song shall ring, The Lord om - nip - o - tent is King.

O Worship the King

P. DODDRIDGE

J. HAYDN

1. O, wor - ship the King, all = glo - rious a - bove! O,
2. Thy boun - ti - ful care what tongue can re - cite? It
3. Frail chil - dren of dust, and fee - ble as frail, In

grate - ful - ly sing His won - der - ful love! Our Shield and De - fend - er, the
breathes in the air, it shines in the light; It streams from the hills, it de -
Thee do we trust, nor find Thee to fail. Thy mer - cies how ten - der! how

An - cient of Days, Pa - vil - ioned in splen - dor, and gird - ed with praise.
scends to the plain, And sweet - ly dis - tils in the dew and the rain.
firm to the end! Our Mak - er, De - fend - er, Re - deem - er, and Friend!

O Holy Father, Friend Unseen

C. ELLIOTT

F. F. FLEMMING

1. O Ho - ly Fa - ther, Friend un - seen! Since on Thine arm Thou bidst me lean,
2. What tho' the world de - ceit - ful prove, And earth - ly friends and joys re - move;

Help me throughout life's chang - ing scene, . . By faith to cling to Thee!
With pa - tient, un - com - plain - ing love . . . Still would I cling to Thee!

Lord, What Offering Shall We Bring

JOHN TAYLOR

C. M. VON WEBER

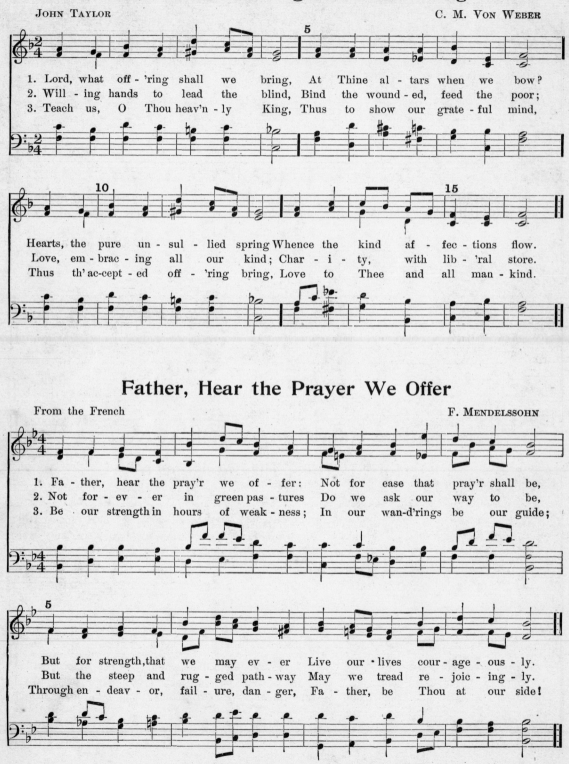

1. Lord, what off - 'ring shall we bring, At Thine al - tars when we bow?
2. Will - ing hands to lead the blind, Bind the wound - ed, feed the poor;
3. Teach us, O Thou heav'n - ly King, Thus to show our grate - ful mind,

Hearts, the pure un - sul - lied spring Whence the kind af - fec - tions flow.
Love, em - brac - ing all our kind; Char - i - ty, with lib - 'ral store.
Thus th' ac - cept - ed off - 'ring bring, Love to Thee and all man - kind.

Father, Hear the Prayer We Offer

From the French

F. MENDELSSOHN

1. Fa - ther, hear the pray'r we of - fer: Not for ease that pray'r shall be,
2. Not for - ev - er in green pas - tures Do we ask our way to be,
3. Be our strength in hours of weak - ness; In our wan - d'rings be our guide;

But for strength, that we may ev - er Live our lives cour - age - ous - ly.
But the steep and rug - ged path - way May we tread re - joic - ing - ly.
Through en - deav - or, fail - ure, dan - ger, Fa - ther, be Thou at our side!

Now Thank We All Our God

M. Rinkart (Tr. Winkworth)

J. Crüger

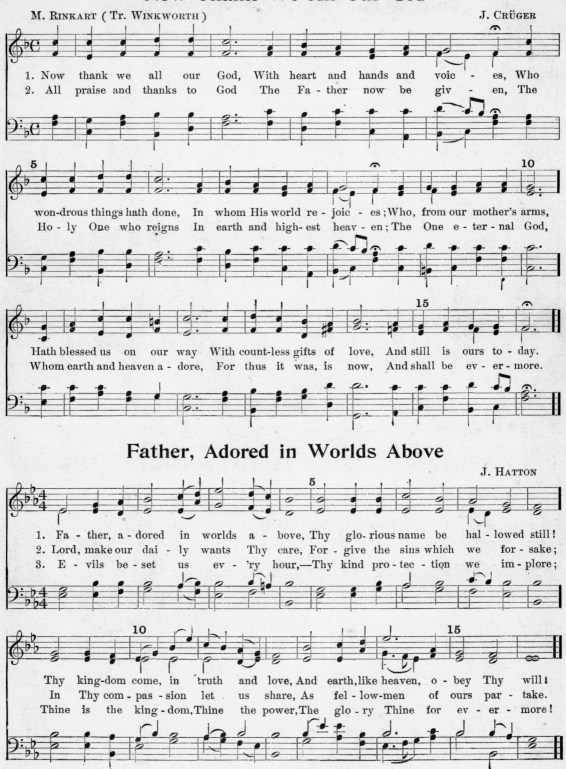

1. Now thank we all our God, With heart and hands and voic - es, Who
2. All praise and thanks to God The Fa - ther now be giv - en, The

won-drous things hath done, In whom His world re - joic - es; Who, from our mother's arms,
Ho - ly One who reigns In earth and high-est heav - en; The One e - ter - nal God,

Hath blessed us on our way With count-less gifts of love, And still is ours to - day.
Whom earth and heaven a - dore, For thus it was, is now, And shall be ev - er - more.

Father, Adored in Worlds Above

J. Hatton

1. Fa - ther, a - dored in worlds a - bove, Thy glo - rious name be hal - lowed still!
2. Lord, make our dai - ly wants Thy care, For - give the sins which we for - sake;
3. E - vils be - set us ev - 'ry hour,—Thy kind pro - tec - tion we im - plore;

Thy king-dom come, in truth and love, And earth, like heaven, o - bey Thy will!
In Thy com - pas - sion let us share, As fel - low-men of ours par - take.
Thine is the king - dom, Thine the power, The glo - ry Thine for ev - er - more!

Anvil Chorus

From " Il Trovatore," GIUSEPPE VERDI

God of the na - tions, in glo - ry en - thron - ed, up - on our lov'd

coun - try Thy bless - ings pour. Guide us and guard us from strife in the

fu - ture, Let Peace dwell a - mong us for ev - er - more!

Proud - ly our ban - ner now gleams with gold - en lus - tre, Bright - er each

star shines in the glo - rious clus - ter — Lib - er - ty for - ev - er -

more! And peace and un - ion, And peace and un - ion, throughout our hap - py land.

If with All Your Hearts

From " Elijah," FELIX MENDELSSOHN

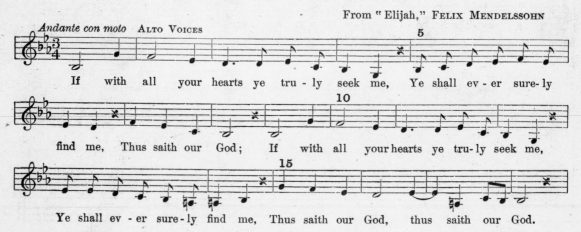

Andante con moto ALTO VOICES

If with all your hearts ye tru - ly seek me, Ye shall ev - er sure - ly

find me, Thus saith our God; If with all your hearts ye tru - ly seek me,

Ye shall ev - er sure - ly find me, Thus saith our God, thus saith our God.

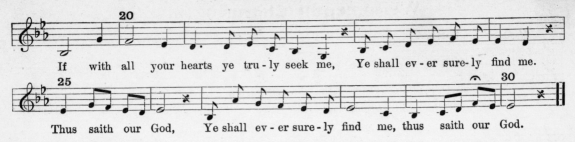

20

If with all your hearts ye tru-ly seek me, Ye shall ev-er sure-ly find me.

25   30

Thus saith our God, Ye shall ev-er sure-ly find me, thus saith our God.

Bonnie Dundee

Scotch Song

Allegretto

1. To the Lords   of Con - ven - tion 'twas Clav - er - house spoke, "Ere the
2. Dun - dee,   he is mount - ed,   he rides   up   the street,   The
3. There are hills   be - yond Pent - land, and lands be - yond Forth;   Be there
4. "Then a - wa'   to the hills,   to the lea,   to the rocks,   Ere I

5

King's crown go down, there are crowns to be broke;   Then each ca - va - lier who loves
bells they ring back - ward, the drums they are beat;   But the pro - vost (douce man) said " Just
lords in the south, there are chiefs in the north;   There are brave Duin - ne - was - sels three
own   a u - surp - er I'll crouch with the fox;   And   trem - ble, false Whigs, in the

hon - or and   me,   Let him fol - low   the   bon - nets   of
e'en let   it   be,   For the town is   well   rid o'   that
thou - sand times three,   Will cry "Hey for the   bon - nets   of
mid'st of   your glee,   Ye hae no   seen   the   last o'   my

10

Bon - nie Dun - dee." Come fill up   my   cup, come fill up   my   can, Come
de'il o' Dun - dee." Come fill up   my   cup, come fill up   my   can, Come
Bon - nie Dun - dee." Come fill up   my   cup, come fill up   my   can, Come
bon - nets and me." Come fill up   my   cup, come fill up   my   can, Come

sad - dle my hors - es, and call out my men, Un - hook the west port, and

15

let us gae free, For its up wi' the bon - nets of Bon - nie Dun - dee!

Welcome, Sweet Springtime

ANTON RUBINSTEIN

Moderato. In Unison

1. Welcome, sweet Springtime! we greet thee in song, Mur-murs of glad-ness fall on the
2. Welcome, bright Springtime! what joy now is ours, Win-ter has fled to far dis-tant

ear; Voi-ces long hush'd now their full notes pro-long, Ech-o-ing far and near;
climes; Flo-ra thy pres-ence a-waits in the bow'rs, Long-ing for thy com-mands;

Sun-shine now wakes all the flow-'rets from sleep, Joy-giv-ing in-cense
Brook-lets are whis-p'ring as on-ward they flow, Songs of de-light at

floats on the air; Snow-drops and prim-rose both tim-id-ly peep, Hail-ing the
thy glad re-turn; Bound-less the wealth thou in love dost be-stow, Ev-er with

glad new year. Balm-y and life-breath-ing breez-es are blow-ing,
lav-ish hands. How na-ture loves thee, each glad voice dis-clos-es,

Swift-ly to na-ture new vig-or be-stow-ing; Ah! how my heart beats with
Her-ald thou art of the time of the ro-ses. Ah! how my heart beats with

rap-ture a-new, As earth's fair-est beau-ties a-gain meet my view.

Sing, then, ye birds, raise your voi-ces on high; Flow-'rets, a-wake ye, burst in-to bloom,

Spring-time is come, and sweet sum-mer is nigh, Sing, then, ye birds, oh, sing!

Then You'll Remember Me

From "The Bohemian Girl"
M. W. Balfe

Andante cantabile

1. When oth-er lips and oth-er hearts their tales of love shall tell, In
2. When cold-ness or de-ceit shall slight the beau-ty now they prize, And

language whose ex-cess im-parts the pow'r they feel so well, There may per-haps in
deem it but a fa-ded light which burns with-in your eyes; When hol-low hearts shall

rall.   a tempo

such a scene some rec-ol-lec-tion be Of days that have as hap-py been, And
wear a mask,'twill break your own to see, In such a mo-ment I but ask that

you'll re-mem-ber me, . . . And you'll re-mem-ber, you'll re-mem-ber me.
you'll re-mem-ber me, . . . That you'll re-mem-ber, you'll re-mem-ber me.

The Harp that once thro' Tara's Halls

Thomas Moore

Irish Song

Andante

1. The harp that once thro' Ta-ra's halls The soul of mu-sic shed, Now
2. No more to chiefs and la-dies bright The harp of Ta-ra swells; The

hangs as mute on Ta-ra's walls As if that soul were fled; So
chords a-lone that break at night, Its tale of ru-in tells. Thus

sleeps the pride of form-er days, So glo-ry's thrill is o'er, And
Free-dom now so sel-dom wakes; The on-ly throb she gives Is

dim.   15

hearts that once beat high for praise, Now feel that pulse no more.
when some heart in-dig-nant breaks, To show that still she lives!

The Heart Bowed Down

From "The Bohemian Girl," M. W. BALFE

Andante

1. The heart bow'd down by weight of woe, To weak-est hopes will
2. The mind will, in its worst de-spair, Still pon-der o'er the

cling, To thought and im-pulse while they flow, That
past, On mo-ments of de-light that were Too

rall.

can no com-fort bring, that can, that can no com-fort
beau-ti-ful to last, that were too beau-ti-ful, too beau-ti-ful to

bring; With these, ex-cit-ing scenes will blend, O'er pleas-ure's path-way
last; To long-de-part-ed years ex-tend Its vis-ions, with them

thrown; But mem-'ry is the on-ly friend That grief can call its
flown, For mem-'ry is the on-ly friend That grief can call its

own, that grief can call its own, that grief can call its own.

Auld Lang Syne

ROBERT BURNS

Scotch Melody

Moderato

1. Should auld ac-quaint-ance be for-got And nev-er brought to mind? Should
2. We've roam'd to-geth-er o'er the mead, A-mong the flow'rs so fine; But
3. Then here's a hand, my trust-y friend, And give a hand of thine, We'll

auld ac-quaint-ance be for-got, And days of Auld Lang Syne? For
o-ceans broad be-tween have roar'd, Since days of Auld Lang Syne! For
have a thought of kind-ness yet, For days of Auld Lang Syne! For

days of Auld Lang Syne, my friend, For days of Auld Lang Syne, We'll
have a thought of kind-ness yet, For days of Auld Lang Syne.

The Hazel Dell

GEORGE F. ROOT

Moderato

1. In the Ha-zel Dell my Nel-ly's sleep-ing, Nel-ly lov'd so
2. In the Ha-zel Dell my Nel-ly's sleep-ing, Where the flow-ers
3. Now I'm wea-ry, friend-less and for-sa-ken, Watch-ing here a-

long, And my lone-ly, lone-ly watch I'm keep-ing, Nel-ly lost and
wave, And the si-lent stars are night-ly weep-ing, O'er poor Nel-ly's
lone; Nel-ly, thou no more will fond-ly cheer me, With thy lov-ing

gone; Here in moon-light oft-en we have wan-der'd Thro' the si-lent
grave; Hopes that once my bos-om fond-ly cher-ished, Smile no more on
tone; Yet for-ev-er shall thy gen-tle im-age In my mem-'ry

shade; Now where leaf-y branch-es droop-ing down-ward, Lit-tle Nel-ly's laid.
me; Ev-'ry dream of joy, a-las, has per-ished, Nel-ly, dear, with thee.
dwell, And my tears thy lone-ly grave shall moist-en, Nel-ly, dear, fare-well!

CHORUS

All a-lone my watch I'm keep-ing In the Ha-zel Dell, For my

dar-ling Nel-ly's near me sleep-ing, Nel-ly dear, fare-well.

Long, Long Ago

Thomas Haynes Bayly

Moderato

1. Tell me the tales that to me were so dear, Long, long a - go,
2. Do you re - mem - ber the path where we met, Long, long a - go,

long, long a - go, Sing me the songs I de - light - ed to hear,
long, long a - go? Ah, yes, you told me you ne'er would for - get,

Long, long a - go, long a - go. Now you are come all my
Long, long a - go, long a - go. Then to all oth - ers my

grief is re - moved; Let me for - get that so long you have rov'd;
smile you pre - ferr'd; Love, when you spoke, gave a charm to each word;

Let me be - lieve that you love as you loved, Long, long a - go, long a - go.
Still my heart treas - ures the prais - es I heard, Long, long a - go, long a - go.

Loch Lomond

Scotch Folksong

Andante

1. By yon bon - nie banks, And by yon bon - nie braes, Where the
2. 'Twas there that we part - ed In yon shad - y glen, On the
3. The wee bird may sing, And the wild flow - ers spring, And in

sun shines bright on Loch Lo - mond, Where me and my true love, Were
steep, steep side of Ben Lo - mond, Where in soft, pur - ple hue, The
sun - shine the wa - ters be sleep - ing, But the bro - ken heart it kens Nae

ev - er want to gae, On the bon - nie, bon - nie banks of Loch
High - land hills we view, And the moon com - ing out in the
sec - ond spring a - gain, Tho' the wae - ful may cease frae their

faster

Lo - mond. Oh, ye'll tak' the high - road and I'll tak' the low - road, And
gloam - ing. Oh, ye'll tak' the high - road and I'll tak' the low - road, And
greet - ing.* Oh, ye'll tak' the high - road and I'll tak' the low - road, And

* Greeting, an old Scotch word for weeping.

Slower

I'll be in Scot-land a-fore ye: But I and my true love will nev-er meet a-gain, On the bon-nie, bon-nie banks of Loch Lo-mond.

Believe Me, if All Those Endearing Young Charms

THOMAS MOORE

DAVENANT

Andante

1. Be - lieve me, if all those en - dear - ing young charms Which I gaze on so fond - ly to - day, Were to change by to - mor - row and fleet in my arms, Like fair - y gifts fad - ing a - way; Thou would'st still be a - dored, as this mo - ment thou art, Let thy love - li - ness fade as it will, And a - round the dear ru - in, each wish of my heart Would en - twine it - self ver - dant - ly still.

2. It is not while beau - ty and youth are thine own, And thy cheeks are pro - faned with a tear, That the fer - vor and faith of a soul can be known, To which time will but make thee more dear! No, the heart that has tru - ly lov'd nev - er for - gets, But as tru - ly loves on to the close; As the sun - flow'r turns on her god when he sets, The same look which she turn'd when he rose.

The Men of Harlech

Welsh Folksong

Maestoso

1. Lo! the glad-some day is break-ing, Beau-ty from her slum-bers wak-ing;
2. Fare ye well, dear na-tive moun-tains, Val-leys green, and flow-ing foun-tains,

Forth to bat-tle, men of Har-lech! On-ward to the fray! Pen-nons gay are
Where the tide of war is rag-ing, Thith-er lies our way. There, 'midst din and

stream-ing, Fal-chions bright-ly gleam-ing; Rush we, like a might-y tor-rent,
clan-gor, Brav-ing foe-man's an-ger; 'Neath the val-iant Gwy-nedd's ban-ner,

cres.

Ne'er of dan-ger dream-ing, On where glo-ry points the way, Where the sun of
In the strife en-gag-ing, Fore-most in the bat-tle fray, Where the sun of

free-dom's shin-ing. Forth to bat-tle, men of Har-lech! On-ward to the fray!
free-dom's shin-ing,— There must be the men of Har-lech! Fore-most in the fray!

The Blue Bells of Scotland

Mrs. JORDAN

Scotch Folksong

Moderato

1. O where, and O where is your High-land lad-die gone? O where, and O
2. O where, and O where did your High-land lad-die dwell? O where, and O
3. But what, and O what if your High-land lad should die? But what, and O

where is your High-land lad-die gone? He's gone to fight the French For King
where did your High-land lad-die dwell? He dwelt in mer-ry Scot-land, At the
what if your High-land lad should die? The bag-pipes should play o'er him, And I'd

dim. *p*

George up-on the throne, And it's O, in my heart I...wish him safe at home!
sign of the Blue Bell, And it's O, in my heart I...love my lad-die well!
sit me down and cry, And it's O, in my heart I...wish he may not die!

INDEX

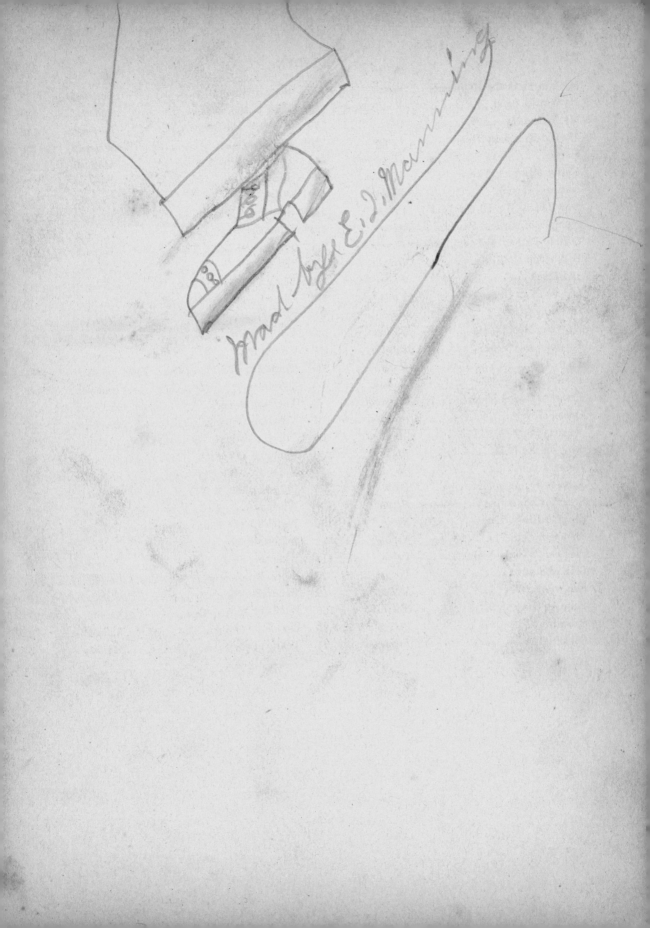